POT CHRYSANTHEMUM PRODUCTION

635.933

Dr Barrie Machin

Grower Guide No. 5
2nd Series

Grower Books
Nexus Media Ltd, Kent

Grower Books
Nexus Media Ltd
Nexus House
Swanley, Kent BR8 8HY

First published 1997

© Grower Books 1997

ISBN 1 899372 10 5

Series editor Peter Rogers.   Production Octavia Wolton.
Publisher Tony Salter.

Printed in Great Britain.

Due care has been taken in the preparation of this book. The information is based on standard industry practice as interpreted by the author; it should not be regarded as a complete production programme nor as the only suitable regime. The publisher and author will not accept responsibility for any outcome arising from the application of the information it contains.

Contents

This book was written for the conditions (daylength, temperature patterns, etc) that apply in the United Kingdom. Much of the information is therefore relevant to chrysanthemum production in northern Europe and northern North America. Growers elsewhere will need to adapt the technical information appropriately.

Abbreviations

mm = millimetre	W = watt	vpm = volumes per million
cm = centimetre	kW = kilowatt	ppm = parts per million
m = metre	mg = milligram	CO_2 = carbon dioxide
sq m = square metre	g = gram	MJ = megajoules
ha = hectare	kg = kilogram	IBA = indolylbutyric acid
HRI = Horticulture Research International		B-Nine = daminozide

Introduction

The forerunner to this book – Year-round Chrysanthemums – dealt with both pot plant production and cut flower production. When it was written – in 1983 – it was still common to find year-round spray chrysanthemums and pot chrysanthemums being grown on the same nursery. Since then commercial practice has changed enormously and growers have specialised more and more. It is far less common for a pot plant grower to grow cut flowers as well and vice versa. Equipping a glasshouse for pot production will not necessarily suit cut flower production and crop management, packing and despatch are quite different.

For these and other reasons the two types of production have polarised and while much of the fundamental science and technology which applies to both is the same, their application is fundamentally different.

So when a revision of Year-round Chrysanthemums was planned, it was decided to separate the two disciplines. The companion to this book – 'Cut Flower Chrysanthemum Production' – therefore contains several chapters in common with this one.

Dr Barrie Machin
1997

I am greatly indebted to Jeff Hooper and the board of Southern Glasshouse Produce Ltd for permission to use facts gained in the course of my work at their Swallowfield Nursery for the last 10 years.

'Cut Flower Chrysanthemum Production' is a uniform Grower Guide in this series, by the same author, available from Grower Books

1 Fundamentals

Background. Management aspects. Resources. Choice of programme.

The year-round chrysanthemum industry can be said to have begun (in the UK at least) around 1955 since when there have been many interesting developments. While the basic scientific principles on which the original growing programmes were based remain valid, a great deal of detailed research has been carried out around the world which has had some effect on basic environmental control techniques. Much more change has taken place, however, in the implementation of scientific research in husbandry practice, as growers have gradually become more experienced in their knowledge of how the chrysanthemum behaves in all types of controlled environments.

This gradual appreciation of plant/environment interactions has inevitably led to the development of more sophisticated programmes, particularly for the environmentally favoured areas and production figures have risen accordingly. For instance in 1957, using a three-and-a-quarter crops a year cut flower programme, it was possible to plant at the rate of 460,000/acre/year when only 55% of the floor area of the glasshouse was planted. By 1977, using varieties which could be programmed to produce four crops a year and making more efficient use of floor area (70%), the number of plants per acre per year had risen to 780,000, an increase in production of almost 70%.

Increases in production of pot plants of a similar scale have also been recorded. In 1958 the number of 14cm pots marketed per acre per year was only 90,000 but by 1968, with the use of mobile benches and different spacing techniques, the figures had risen sharply to over 200,000.

In view of the increasing efficiency of production it seems incredible that in 1992 the UK industry was passing through the worst financial crisis in its history. The extremely high rate of cost inflation affecting the growers' main production items was largely to blame. This book takes as its main theme the urgent and continuing need to maximise high quality production with the minimum cost of input per stem.

Today the need for maximum efficiency is accompanied by a greater emphasis on quality and good shelf life.

Each section of this book emphasises the best cultural technique to produce top quality plants and, perhaps more importantly, the best methods to maximise profit. Discerning growers will know these two admirable concepts are not always compatible. Where this is the case the text makes it abundantly clear.

Flexibility in programming and husbandry is essential and growing techniques must improve as new varieties and research indicate the most profitable production systems.

New programmes

Growers intending to attempt year-round production for the first time, or those developing a new site, have a golden opportunity to learn from all the past mistakes and knowledge gained since 1955. For example it is vital for the grower to give a lot of thought to all aspects of the enterprise before going ahead.

Year-round production involves over five crops of pot plants from the same area each year. This makes it one of the most intensive production systems in horticulture. At the outset, therefore, the grower must honestly consider both his desire and ability to manage a production programme that demands he does the right thing in the right way at the right time every week of the year.

There is little margin for error and little time to correct errors. If the motivation and interest is there but not the management expertise (and this is a very difficult personal decision to make) then the grower-owner should appoint a suitably experienced manager responsible for all aspects of programming, environmental and husbandry control.

The optimum combination of management personnel for a year-round chrysanthemum programme is a businessman, a grower, an engineer and a salesman. There are few, if any, horticulturists, let alone chrysanthemum growers, who can fill all four roles adequately themselves, yet good management in all these aspects is essential for economic success. The first objective, therefore, is to know yourself and to make suitable additions to staff to complement your own knowledge and expertise.

It is possible, of course, to sub-contract the engineering requirements but there is no avoiding the basic fact that a sound, economic programme can only be based on good business sense, excellent growing technique and positive, aggressive selling.

Re-assessment of glasshouses

Some year-round pot programmes have been occupying the same glasshouses for 20 to 25 years and many have been in continual production on the same site for over 10 years. These growers should consider the wisdom of continuing these programmes in out-of-date glasshouses in which environmental control falls short of the accuracy required.

For instance some of the original programmes were begun in glasshouse blocks with height to gutter dimensions unsuitable for the installation of thermal screens which can save up to 50% of the fuel costs. Other, more modern glasshouses were so designed that thermal screen installation cut out too much winter light at the south end of benches and under the gutters. This could mean a loss in quality of 5% of the crop at a time when production is particularly expensive.

In glasshouses designed with thermal screens in mind, and with up-to-date environmental control and husbandry practices, the fastest production programmes can be used with some confidence that revenue will outweigh costs. In older houses, which now fall far short of optimum requirements, programming will have to take this into account if year-round pot chrysanthemum production is to continue.

Slightly slower programmes using certain varieties can be planned for these houses, in which plant growth is not so critically dependent for quality on daylight admission and night temperature control at 18C or 19C.

However bearing in mind that profit margins are constantly squeezed by rising costs, especially labour, only the most modern production units will be viable in future.

A critical measurement in glasshouses is height to the gutters. Some of the largest UK growers are still using houses converted to all year round production from other crops in which height to gutters varies from 2.6 to 2.75m. At the time of writing, one of the most modern glasshouses producing year-round chrysanthemums and built in the 1990's employs a height to gutter of 3.25m and a house to be built this year in the UK has provision for gutters 4.3m high. This extra height will allow ample space for all overhead equipment, including up-to-date thermal screens, so that not only maximum saving of heat will be achieved but a greater volume of air will be enclosed. This is important, especially in summer conditions when high night temperatures are a problem. Greater height to gutters always means that conditions within the glasshouse are less liable to fluctuations and this makes good crops easier to grow.

Types of programmes

Not only will age and design of glasshouses affect the production plan, but also the size of the holding and the number of glasshouses available. As fuel costs have risen large glasshouses – 0.2ha (half-an-acre) blocks or larger – are at a disadvantage compared with programmes made up of a number of smaller houses.

It is now well known that if temperatures are maintained at the optimum level for bud development during the first four weeks of short-days, lower than optimum temperatures will have little adverse effect on the crop especially when given after this most critical period. This knowledge makes it possible to improve programming and save fuel costs.

In houses which hold just one or two weekly pottings, a far greater fuel saving is possible compared with programmes in larger areas of glass which hold over 50% of the programme or even all of it.

In very big glasshouses, housing a large percentage of the nursery's production, it will probably be better to use varieties most tolerant of night temperatures lower than 18C on a slower schedule in winter, than attempt fast production without the means to conserve fuel during those periods of growth where fuel saving is possible. If large areas of glass can be fitted with sectional heating and mobile plastic screens, then faster programmes with higher night temperatures can be used.

These are some of the factors that well-established growers should consider before going into another winter using the same pot programme in the same glasshouses. Careful thought given to all aspects of year-round production, especially those of environmental control and efficiency of husbandry, may lead to more sensible decisions on programming which will give the crop a much better chance for profitability in the future.

HOW IT BEGAN

The history of chrysanthemum production is a fascinating one. Originating in China over 3,000 years ago, chrysanthemums became prominent from 800AD in Japan where many forms were developed.

However it was not until 200 years ago that plants were brought to Europe arriving by sea in southern France and gradually migrating to Holland and the UK before the end of the 18th century. And some time in the 1850's chrysanthemums were introduced to the USA. In each country different types were developed according to popular demand.

It was in France especially that dwarf, short-jointed well-branched decorative varieties were developed for growing in pots for the All Saints Day market, varieties such as Blanche de Poitevene and Primrose Poitou.

The Americans, whose market is now the biggest for pot chrysanthemums in the world, developed their own varieties but also acquired some French ones, giving them names such as Delaware and Oregon. These varieties were re-introduced to Europe in the late 1950's when year-round pot production started in Sussex.

Enter photoperiodism

However the whole scene had changed in the USA in the 1920's and 30's following the discover of photoperiodism in 1920. American growers learned first to delay flowering by the use of lights at night, and then to cover the plants with black cloth at night to bring forward the flowering of late varieties into August and September. Then in 1946, in Ohio, the first year-round cut flower programme was devised using one plant for each flower at close spacing. Because of the requirement for large quantities of cuttings each week for each grower, the propagation industry as we now know it developed at the same time. Year-round pot production soon followed.

American spray varieties and the methods of stock production and propagation were introduced to the UK in 1955 at Frampton's Nurseries Ltd and AG Sparkes Ltd. Within two years the first pot programme at Normans Nurseries, Littlehampton, was begun using American varieties and the Princess Anne family bred by Harry Shoesmith.

The American method was to 'snap' cuttings from stock plants kept vegetative by night-break lighting and to root these in benches filled with 50% peat and 50% course grit. These first growers of year-round chrysanthemums in Europe had to develop stock production areas to cope with the weekly requirement for cuttings and inevitably became the first propagators as other growers became interested in crop.

From a nucleus of about 15 growers in 1960 year-round growing in Britain increased rapidly and in 1962 Dutch growers followed suit. Very soon after this, pot production started in Denmark.

American growers generally use five plants around a 6in (15.2cm) pot. These are later pinched to provide about 20 disbudded (increasingly not disbudded) blooms per pot. Some specialist American producers use seven plants per pot grown single stem and kept short by growth regulators to provide seven large disbudded flowers, usually decoratives, per pot.

Since cut flower chrysanthemums used by American and Canadian markets are now mainly grown in Costa Rica and Colombia, a very high proportion of American chrysanthemum growers produce plants in pots.

Pot chrysanthemum production in Europe is mainly confined to the UK and Denmark with a few growers in Holland. In the UK the pot chrysanthemum industry, having first tried the full range of pot sizes, quickly decided that the use of five plants (later pinched) per 14cm half-pot gave the best returns for growers and best satisfied the consumers. In Denmark and Holland pot chrysanthemum growers use either three plants in a 10cm pot or one plant in a 7.5 or 9cm pot, all then pinched to provide and all-round, decorative effect.

Competitive edge

Pot chrysanthemum growers should be thankful that, for reasons of transport costs from Colombia and for aesthetic reasons in Japan, import compe;tition is unlikely to surge from South America and the far east the way it has with cut flower chrysanthemums. In America, when cut flower chrysanthemum production moved south, there was an immediate increase in pot production in glasshouses in the northern and western USA. The other main pot chrysanthemum production areas are in the UK and Denmark with some in Holland.

At about the same time the Dutch started year-round cut flower chrysanthemum production, some Colombian growers copied the American system and were soon exporting large quantities of flowers to the USA. Cut flower production in the USA, which began in the mid-west, had been driven south and west to Florida and California by rising labour costs and the better light conditions which suited the production of quality flowers. However it soon became apparent that cheaper production still was possible even further south and production in countries like Costa Rica and Colombia soared.

The conditions in the high Andes of South America were found to be especially favourable for growing cut flowers. As well as cheap labour there was a large area of suitably flat land, adequate water and a constant short-day environment where night length only varied from 12 to 12.5 hours. This, of course, avoided the expensive blackout systems required in more northerly countries. The only problem was that natural night temperatures were on the low side.

The combination of low night temperatures and, at times long nights (up to 11.5-hours) produced stems with fewer flowers and longer pedicels than the more controlled glasshouse regimes of nurseries in the north. However these suited the American cut flower market very well. American consumers appreciated large flowers with pedicels up to 22cm in length.

Luckily for growers in Europe long pedicelled stems with few flowers are less acceptable to the consumer. This fact also ensures that it is unlikely that pot chrysanthemum production will be attempted in South America. The uncontrolled climate cannot produce short pot plants with sufficient flower cover. The use of day length and temperature control to achieve suitable plants would add to the high transport costs and render the pot crop unviable.

Full circle

Much chrysanthemum production in Japan still uses traditional techniques of planting and pinching at various times of the year to maintain continuous production. This is possible because of the country's widely different environments from Okinawa in the south to Hokkaido in the north.

However in 1975 Dr Kawata, a leading chrysanthemum expert, visited the UK and Holland and was instrumental in starting year-round production in Japan using single spray varieties. He used American and Dutch varieties and bred some himself. Of a total of 3,000ha in production in Japan, over 10% is now controlled year-round production of single, anemone and quill spray types mainly based in the north of the main island, Honshu. The plants are still mostly pinched for two stems because many Japanese-bred varieties have low long-day leaf numbers and would produce compound sprays on single stems.

Some leading Japanese growers, however, are now using single stem production and experimenting with plants grown in nutrified blocks of compost; and some are trying European varieties.

Colombian growers are also beginning to use European varieties in greater quantity and to develop the European propagation system originated by the author.

Traditionally Japanese growers produced their own cuttings but now cuttings are being imported from as far away as South Africa. And chrysanthemum stock production areas will soon be developed in China for the Japanese market. Then, almost certainly, year-round flower production will begin in China and the worldwide travels of the chrysanthemum will have turned full circle.

None of the production areas outside Europe and North America grow pot chrysanthemums in any quantity but if year-round chrysanthemum production begins in China it is likely that pot chrysanthemums will be required. Allen Jackson of Wye College did some breeding with Chinese pot varieties in the 1960's and the gene pool from them is still available to pot chrysanthemum breeders today.

2 Environmental factors

Glasshouse regimes. Daylength. Night-break lighting. Lighting installations. Blackout regimes. Temperatures. Carbon dioxide enrichment. Humidity. Root environment. Nutrition.

The growth and development of chrysanthemum plants are affected by all the main factors of both the aerial and root environments. Optimum plant growth will only be achieved if all environmental factors are balanced in relation to the needs of the pot chrysanthemum crop. The same applies to stock plants for cuttings production (see chapter 4).

Since year-round chrysanthemum production began in the late 1950's, much research has been carried out into the specific requirements of the crop. In the UK this work was carried out in the south, where the greater part of the industry is located.

This work, together with that in other countries (particularly in the USA where research into reactions of chrysanthemums to the environment has been continuous since 1920), has given us sufficient information to be able to control growth of the plants so that year-round production programmes can be carried out with confidence. Research continues to add to our knowledge, and refinements to production techniques leading to greater efficiency and to improved cropping continue to be made.

DAYLENGTH

The discovery that flowering of chrysanthemums was governed by the length of the day was an essential breakthrough in 1920. Research on daylength responses has continued since then and is currently continuing at the Naaldwijk experimental station in the Netherlands.

Daylength is normally defined as the duration of the light period from sunrise to sunset. Because chrysanthemums were found to flower when the days were decreasing in length, they were classified as 'short-day' plants.

Varietal response

It has to be understood at the outset that the varieties of chrysanthemum currently used in year-round programmes are those which flower naturally from mid-October to mid-November and fall into the 'mid-season' category as defined by the National Chrysanthemum Society of Great Britain. 'Early flowering' varieties ('garden' varieties in the USA), flower naturally outdoors from July to September with flowering mainly governed by temperature conditions.

Although recent work in the UK – at Horticulture Research International – has shown that early flowering varieties are to some extent responsive to daylength, it is those varieties in which flowering is dependent on daylength that we are concerned with here.

The flowering response of mid-season varieties has been defined as the number of weeks of short-days from their commencement to the time when the flower is ready for marketing under average night temperatures (ie 16C) and average daylight (eg October) conditions. These response categories are summarised in the panel.

Response categories

Response group	Natural flowering date
7-week	October 5 to October 14
8-week	October 15 to October 24
9-week	October 25 to November 4
10-week	November 5 to November 14
11-week	November 15 to November 24

Short-day conditions

Research soon showed that chrysanthemums initiate flower buds when the length of day shortens to less than 14.5 hours and develop these buds when daylength further decreases to 13.5 hours or less.

A major breakthrough occurred when it was discovered that it is the length of the dark period and not the light period that actually causes the switch over to the flowering condition. In other words, night lengths exceeding 9.5 hours initiate flower buds and night lengths of 10.5 hours or more develop them.

NIGHT-BREAK LIGHTING

The most effective method of *preventing* flower bud initiation when plants have to be kept vegetative has, therefore, been found to be the use of artificial light during the night to produce two dark periods shorter than 9.5 hours. To be safe, we ensure that they are actually less than 8 hours.

It does not matter if the sum of the two dark periods exceeds the critical number of hours, provided neither individual dark period does so.

Early research showed that the lights could be switched on at midnight for several hours and this would keep the plants vegetative during natural short days. In recent years lights have been switched on automatically to bisect the night almost exactly, eg from 10pm to 2am. There is, however, no experimental evidence to show that this is necessary. Indeed a trial at HRI Efford in Hampshire (Efford EHS as it was then, in February 1982) indicated that the use of artificial light from midnight onwards is as effective in preventing premature budding in natural short days as an artificial light period spaced equally on either side of midnight. This means that growers can benefit from the cheaper electrical tariff that, in the UK, normally applies between midnight and 7am.

It is clear, then, that chrysanthemums are actually 'long-night' rather than 'short-day' plants but because the latter term has been in use for many years and is fully understood, it will continue to be used in this book.

Nights are naturally too long for vegetative growth to occur from mid-August to mid-April but to make sure that growth is under full control, night-break lighting should be used from approximately August 2 to May 2. Some propagators and growers continue to use night-break lighting during May, June and July but there are neither experimental nor practical reasons for this in Britain and under normal conditions the expense of lighting can be saved. Actually because most year-round growers in Europe now use automatic blackout systems which cover the whole glasshouse in summer, lamps have to be used (4 hours) under the blackout where long-day conditions are required.

It is, however, extremely important that the plants receive the correct amount of light during the night-break period from August to April, the number of hours of lighting increasing as the length of the natural dark period increases.

Night-break schedule

	Night-break lighting
August, September, April, May	2 hours
October, March	3 hours
November, December, January, February	4 hours

The number of hours shown in the panel are correct for continuous periods of light where the lighting installation provides illumination of not less that 110 lux at the leaves of the plants furthest from the light source. Some installations provide illuminances between 60 and 110 lux over the plants furthest from the light source. In these cases it is wise to increase the number of hours given by one hour in each case to ensure full control over vegetative growth.

Cyclic lighting

It is known that the inhibiting effect of night-break lighting continues for a short period after the lamps are switched off so it is now considered unnecessary to give continuous illumination during the lighting phase.

However research in Britain and the USA has laid down definite guidelines. For instance the plants must be illuminated at least every 30 minutes and in Britain it is now standard practice to use a certain percentage of light every 30 minutes, as follows:

> *For installations providing not less than 100 lux illuminance*
> 10 minutes of continuous light in each 30-minute cycle

> *For installations providing 60 to 100 lux illuminance*
> 15 minutes of continuous light in each 30-minute cycle

In both the above systems, 4 hours of lighting are necessary from August to October and from March to May, and 5 hours of lighting for November, December and January. Each period should begin and end with a light period.

For stock plants under cyclic lighting it is recommended that 50% cycles using 110 lux illuminance should be used.

Type of lamp and spacing

Normal domestic type tungsten filament or incandescent coil lamps are entirely suitable for night-break lighting.

Over single benches up to 1.5m wide, 100W lamps can be used, spaced 1.8m apart and 1.2 to 1.4m above the tips of the plants. In larger areas such as the propagation floor, it is more efficient to use 150W lamps and these should be spaced 3.1m apart each way and 1.5 to 1.8m above the plants.

Varietal differences

Work at HRI in Britain has shown that some cut flower varieties require greater illuminance than the majority during the night-break lighting period to prevent budding in natural short-days. The variety Snowdon, for instance, requires illuminance of 150 lux to prevent budding, compared with a more typical variety, Polaris, which is prevented from budding by illuminance of 100 lux during night-break lighting.

These varietal differences are particularly important to propagators in southern latitudes where daylight intensities are high during natural short-days.

Although there is no evidence of differing lighting requirements for pot varieties it is wise to assume that pot varieties with a similar reaction to Snowdon do exist.

The pot crop is a very valuable one and premature budding on some plants before positive short days are applied would greatly reduce quality and hence profitability.

Thus, propagation and long-day areas used for pot plant production should be supplied with 150 lux of illuminance during the night period.

Both high pressure and low pressure sodium lamps can be used effectively for night-break lighting. Lighting is, of course, continuous and has to be in the order of 300 lux, ie double the illuminance required for tungsten lighting installations.

However because a sodium lamp can produce more than eight times the illuminance of a tungsten lamp with the same electrical power consumption, the use of sodium lamps represents a considerable saving in running costs. But their use for night-break lighting applies more to stock production than to flowering areas, for practical reasons, like the number of beds or benches per unit in the glasshouse.

Light spill

While it has been shown that illuminances of up to 150 lux are necessary to prevent flower bud initiation in natural short-day conditions, it is possible to delay flowering in plants which are developing flower buds if these are exposed to illuminances of as little as 20 lux. It is essential, therefore, that where lamps are being used at night to keep plants in a vegetative condition, adjacent benches on which flower buds are being initiated must not be allowed to receive any 'light spill'.

Light spill can be prevented by the use of a drop cloth which divides the long-day and short-day areas.

The lighting installation

The actual area of night-break lighting required in each programme will vary according to the type of programme used and the period of vegetative growth allowed for each crop, particularly during the periods of poorest natural light (see page 39) For a relatively slow, 3.5 crop/year cut flower programme, up to 730m of cable (either 7/.067 VR flat twin or 7/.067 PCP sheathed flat twin) with 400 lamps of 100W each will be in use at any one time. This represents a current loading of 100kW/ha.

Compared with the slowest cut flower crop, pot plant programmes require only about 25% of the area of night-break lighting because only one or at most two weeks of long-days are required after propagation on certain varieties in poor light conditions.

Moreover those pots are all at fairly close spacing at the time. However the situation regarding electrical requirement and current loading becomes more complicated because of the increasing use of supplementary light over many winter pot crops (see page 24) and qualified advice as to loading should be sought.

However where current loading is a limiting factor, the use of cyclic night-break lighting has frequently been found to overcome the problem, but in all cases it is best that the lighting equipment be installed by a qualified electrical engineer.

BLACKING-OUT

To ensure the most rapid initiation and early development of flower buds, there must be positive daylength control from mid-March to mid-September for all pot varieties. Back in the 1920's plants were wheeled in and out of dark rooms to achieve this daylength control.

After years of research into the best type of material for exclusion of light, the timing of darkening and the number of weeks of darkening necessary, we now have a clear understanding of the best method. Not only must light be excluded from the plants but the material used must be easily moved back and forth.

Since the first edition of this book, screens have become available which are constructed of two layers of metallised plastic and operated automatically under computer control according to the length of the night required.

Time of blacking-out

When to blackout is very important in relation to the quality of the flowering plant and to the response time of the crop. Blacking-out at either end of the day is best, not only because of the practical problem of labour usage but also because the light rays strike the darkening material more obliquely than nearer midday and less light passes through.

In Britain it has been found ideal to allow the plants an 11-hour day. Less time than this reduces the quality of the crop and more time can delay flowering to some extent.

The covers are normally best removed at 7am (0700) and the plants re-covered at 6pm (1800). With automatic blackout systems this timing can be precise but growers using hand-operated blackout systems must straddle the optimum times to obtain the best results.

Every effort should be made to avoid covering plants too early (for example, to save overtime rates) as this may seriously damage plants due to high temperatures under the blackout in the early evening. It has been known for the tips of plants to be completely scorched by hand covering with black polythene at 5pm (1700) in midsummer.

Period of blacking-out

The earliest flowering response is achieved by blacking-out every day of the week and this is no problem where automatic systems are installed.

For many years, especially where hand blacking-out was the norm, blacking-out for just six days a week was regarded as commercially acceptable. However the penalty is a flowering delay of from three to seven days according to season and it is extremely doubtful if this can be economically acceptable today.

It is unnecessary and even damaging to the crop to use blackout right through to harvesting although this often happens with automatic systems. In the later stages of cropping in summer, the cooler the nights the better the size and colour of flowers. It is known that flowering response is irreversible after six weeks of short-days and blackout can, therefore, cease (if the automatic system will allow it) one week after disbudding even in mid-summer without incurring a flowering delay.

Disbudding (if done) is normally carried out about six or seven weeks after the start of short-days depending on the speed of response of the variety.

Automatic blackout

A number of automated blackout systems have been devised. These normally serve the twin objectives of providing artificial long nights in summer and a thermal screen in winter. These systems are continually being improved, as are the metallised plastics which constitute the covering material.

Any grower who is thinking of installing an automatic blackout system would be wise to investigate thoroughly and to cost out all the options available using expert advice.

The use of automatic blackout, quite apart from its dual purpose, has a number of advantages over hand-operated blackouts. Not only is the operation completed in a few minutes and is therefore done at the correct time, but it is also possible to open the covers after dark and to close them again before dawn by means of a time switch. This prevents the build-up of moisture under the covers which helps to keep humidity low and fungal diseases at bay. It also reduces night temperature in summer and improves flower quality.

Uncovering at night also limits the possibility of rain water seeping through the panes in the glasshouse and collecting in impermeable black polythene sheeting, where this is still used.

New covering materials have now been developed to allow the passage of water through the covers without diluting the material's blackout and thermal screening qualities.

It is, of course, necessary to ensure that any holes which become worn in the blackout are mended immediately, particularly those which have occurred in the top surface. A shaft of light falling on the upper leaves of plants will completely inhibit flowering even if leaves nearer the pot are in short-day conditions. Conversely light reaching the basal leaves of a plant which is otherwise shaded will have virtually no effect on its flowering response.

Thermoperiod treatments

Treatment	Temperature	
	Night	Day
1	20C	20C
2	15C	15C
3	10C	20C
4	20C	10C
5	10C	10C

TEMPERATURE

Temperature is one of the main factors of the aerial environment controlling plant growth. It has a profound effect on the rate and quality of growth and hence on the efficiency of the programme and the production capabilities. However because fuel costs are now as high as 20% of the total costs of a pot plant programme, even when all fuel saving systems are taken into account, it is very important that the plants receive temperatures no higher than necessary at any given time.

Aerial temperature needs to be controlled carefully in relation to daily amounts of light, carbon dioxide levels and humidity, and must never be considered as a separate entity. If light is so poor that carbon assimilation is low or non-existent, high temperatures merely lengthen growth and weaken plants.

It does no harm to use slightly lower temperatures for a period on dull days because recent findings suggest that chrysanthemums are capable of averaging out temperature over a period of 48 hours and reacting accordingly.

Night temperature controls bud development rate and temperature during the light period governs the rate of photosynthesis and hence the stem growth rate. It is, therefore, important to integrate temperature conditions over the whole 24 hour period to obtain the best results.

Experiments by Dr Cockshull at HRI in the early 1980's, for instance, showed that thermoperiods have a positive effect on plant response. Using 12 hours for each temperature period, Cockshull grew plants of five 10-week spray varieties in five different thermoperiods (panel, page 15).

Treatment 3 produced tall plants with long internodes and pedicels indicating that stem extension is actually controlled by day temperature and not night temperature as had been thought. Treatments 1 and 4 produced the most flowers per stem, showing that the number of flower buds initiated and developed are increased by a higher night temperature. Treatment 2 had more flowers than Treatments 3 and 5.

The short-day response was governed by the mean temperature so that Treatments 2, 3 and 4 flowered at the same time. Treatment 1 flowered earliest and Treatment 5 flowered last.

The implication of these results for pot chrysanthemum growers are rather obvious. Conditions such as those which cause stretching (treatment 3) and late flowering (Treatment 5) should be avoided and those which promote balanced growth with a good bud set should be provided.

Therefore a mean between Treatments 1 and 2 – ie 18C night, 18C day (noon) to 24C in sun with CO_2 enrichment – is best for good pot chrysanthemum production.

Efford fuel-saving regime

Period	Temperature	
	Night	Day
November	15.5C	15.5C
December	17.0C	15.5C
January	17.0C	15.5C
February	15.0C	15.5C
March to October	13.0C	15.5C

Ventilate at 21.0C

Efford regime

During the fuel crisis of the 1970's, oil costs rose by 400% and this much higher cost of fuel relative to other costs such as cuttings and labour remained for the next 10 years. During this period much valuable research at Efford on cut flower varieties showed growers how they could reduce fuel costs by careful adjustments to night temperatures while still achieving a relatively high quality crop in a reasonable time period.

The recommendations from the former Efford EHS are shown in the panel. The temperatures were for 10-week varieties and were especially important for the first four weeks of short-day conditions. Thereafter, if the production system allowed, night temperatures were reduced by 1 or 2C with no loss of cropping time or quality.

A very important fuel saving was made by using one cold night per week, setting the thermostat down to 4C. This represented a 10% saving of fuel with no delay to the crop.

With the help of thermal screens during the winter period, the fuel savings achieved with Efford regimes have been up to 40%.

Pot plant growers also found these results very useful in saving fuel so long as any delay in cropping did not result in too much stretching for any particular variety. Extra growth regulation sometimes had to be used to compensate for taller growth in some varieties such as Purple Anne.

Night temperature control

Happily in recent years the price of oil and other heating costs have fallen and, with the use of ever increasingly efficient thermal screens and precise control of night temperature by computer, heating costs are now only about 18% of total costs. The concept of night temperature control has, therefore, changed.

During the period of the Efford EHS work, growers needed to use the minimum night temperature conducive to the production of a good crop. Now leading growers want to use the best night temperature possible to produce the fastest, heaviest and most reliable crops of the varieties they wish to grow in their production areas for their market.

For any particular variety, night temperature requirements are always related to daylight quality.

On the south coast of England, normal winter light regimes mean that night temperatures of 18C minimum are suitable for winter production. In Holland, at a higher latitude, night temperatures of 19C or even 20C are required.

These high night temperatures need only apply to the mid-winter period and, as the Efford work tended to show, lower temperatures (17C or even 16C) give good results prior to mid-November and after mid-February flowering for many varieties.

Low temperature tolerance

Growers in the more northern parts of Britain or those who do not have efficient thermal screens or computer control can continue to use the Efford regime effectively. Also, because breeders were very mindful of low temperature tolerance in the recent past, there are a number of varieties capable of being grown in a reasonable timescale in lower than optimum (ie 15C to 17C) night temperatures. Breeders' lists now indicate the low temperature tolerant varieties.

Although the need for low temperature tolerance has been reduced recently in North Europe, breeders will continue to screen positively for this characteristic.

Work carried out at Efford in the late 1980's showed that the Princess Anne varieties were tolerant of low night temperatures (13.3C) for bud set and flowering response. The fact that the plants were disbudded to the main flower bud on each shoot would have helped to keep the plants from becoming too vegetative.

Princess Anne varieties do not now feature in many programmes, so there is less opportunity to save fuel. However with winter crops of modern varieties being supplied with supplementary light, a slight lowering of night temperature occasionally, whether intended or accidental, does not cause serious problems.

Flower quality

Finally it should not be forgotten that, so far as flower quality is concerned, chrysanthemums favour lower rather than higher temperatures for flower development. Low night temperatures (10C to 12C) are far less damaging to flower quality than are high temperatures, eg 20C to 25C at night and up to 35C by day.

From June to September the main factor reducing flower quality is high temperature by night under the blackout covers. Where covers can be drawn back after dark and replaced before dawn by means of a computer or time switch, quality will be improved. Early covering – 5pm (1700) – is not to be recommended despite staff problems where manual covering is still done.

The best compromise is probably to cover from 6pm to 7am (1800 to 0700), so that staff can work on the crop early in the morning. The author's plants are always covered from 7pm to 8am (1900 to 0800), as this is the period that allows the least build-up of heat at night and there is only a short period of heat build-up in the

Sources of carbon dioxide

Kerosene (paraffin)
The sulphur content in the paraffin should be below 0.04%. 4.5 litres of paraffin burn to give 11.24kg CO_2.

Propane
Propane is piped from storage tanks to burners suspended over the crop. The supply pipes to the burners must be correctly installed; if leaks occur, the 35% propylene in the gas before combustion can damage the crop. 2.2kg of propane produces 6.6kg CO_2.

Pure CO$_2$
Pure CO_2 is the safest source and is distributed either from cylinders or a liquifier (using solid CO_2) via 12.7mm rigid PVC pipe around the perimeter of the glasshouse. It is, however, the most expensive source because the storage tanks are pressure vessels and incur considerable capital cost. Pure CO_2 can only be justified on larger nurseries (over 1.2ha).

Natural gas
Natural gas is a safe and useful source of CO_2 if supplies are available.

morning before the covers are removed.

Of course computerised nurseries can have screens removed after dark and returned over the crop before dawn.

CARBON DIOXIDE

On many winter days there is sufficient light and warmth for good growth but, when ventilators remain closed to preserve heat, the plants rapidly use up the CO_2 in the atmosphere which is not replaced sufficiently quickly to maintain a reasonable photosynthetic rate.

There is now sufficient evidence – gathered at Efford EHS over a number of years – to show that CO_2 enrichment is an essential part of the growing programme for year-round chrysanthemums from mid-October to mid-April. Yields of spray chrysanthemums have been increased, on average, by 12% during the this period by CO_2 enrichment. With pot plants it is the individual quality of each pot which is improved.

CO_2 does not compensate for low night temperatures so the CO_2 enrichment programme must be used in conjunction with adequate night temperatures. While CO_2 does not compensate for low light, there is evidence that enrichment with pure CO_2 is worthwhile even on very dull days. By increasing the rate of plant development and leaf area, CO_2 enrichment produces four specific benefits for a pot plant crop:
* improved uniformity of budset
* improved flower quality
* increased number of flowers
* improved leaf quality

The net result is a better grade-out of pots by both improvement in general quality and in reduction in the amount of waste. There is a further advantage in that flowering response is improved by two or three days.

Enrichment rate

The level of carbon dioxide enrichment is 1,000vpm from mid-October to mid-April, from dawn to within an hour and a half of dusk. With pure CO_2, the plants benefit regardless of light conditions but with paraffin there might be a build-up of nitrogen oxides in poor light. With these hydrocarbon fuels, therefore, enrichment should not occur when light is very poor.

It is wise to cease enrichment sufficiently before dusk to allow, perhaps, a brief spell of ventilation to lower humidity before nightfall.

Burning rate

To maintain 1,000vpm CO_2 the burning rate is based on 5.6g/sq m/hour CO_2. If glasshouses are well-sealed and airtight, the burning rate can be reduced to 5.0g/sq m/hour.

HUMIDITY

Relative humidity is the degree of saturation of air with water vapour and is extremely important to the growth of the chrysanthemums within a confined space. Chrysanthemums grow well within limits of relative humidity from 70 to 90% but extremes must be avoided.

Low humidities put a strain on the transpiration and respiration processes in the plant and some of the energy of the plant will be diverted away from actual growth.

Humidities in excess of 90% result in soft growth and in conditions which favour fungal growth. In a situation where diseases like white rust are becoming a real problem, control of humidity is an important requirement.

Water systems which deliver water as drips to the pot surface are to be preferred to those – like overhead spraying – which thoroughly soak the foliage. And at periods of high humidity watering should be carried out in the morning to allow foliage to dry before dusk.

Computerised nurseries have the advantage of early alert to high humidity conditions and steps can be taken to reduce humidity rapidly.

THE ROOT ENVIRONMENT

The root environment consists of the actual substrate in which the roots grow and the moisture, air and nutrient content of the substrate. This is a complex interacting set of environmental factors which could be the subject of a separate book. However for the purposes of producing good quality chrysanthemums it is important to understand the basic concepts of a good root environment.

Plants grow when the sugar produced in the leaves by photosynthesis is converted into energy by respiration. This energy is used to combine the major and minor elements of nutrition into complex proteins for use in building new cells and for other functions within the plant. For instance all hormones which are essential for the plant's natural reactions to its environment and all the pigments – the chlorophyll in leaves, for example, and the anthcyanin and chromatin in flowers – are manufactured from the basic raw materials derived from the soil through a healthy root system.

Nutrients actually enter the plant through the root hairs which are single elongated cells on the surface of the roots, near the tips. The sap in these cells is a more concentrated solution than that of the relatively weak soil solution which surrounds them.

The weak solution passes through the cell wall into the strong solution by a process known as osmosis. Osmosis will, however, only occur if the root hair is healthy and for a root hair to remain healthy it requires oxygen. At the same time an adequate supply of all the nutrients must be in close proximity to the root hairs.

The environment around the root hairs must, therefore, be in reasonable balance between water and air to prevent excessive drying on the one hand and waterlogging and inadequate aeration on the other. For osmosis to occur at the maximum

Availability profile of nutrients

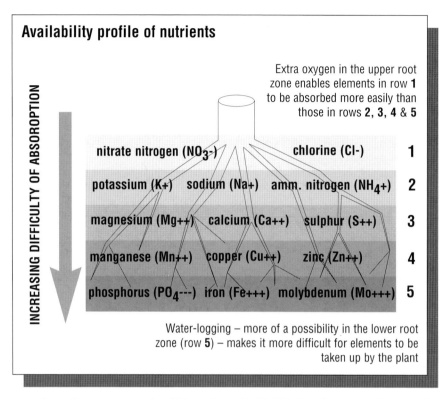

Extra oxygen in the upper root zone enables elements in row **1** to be absorbed more easily than those in rows **2, 3, 4 & 5**

INCREASING DIFFICULTY OF ABSORPTION

nitrate nitrogen (NO$_3$-)   chlorine (Cl-)   **1**

potassium (K+) sodium (Na+) amm. nitrogen (NH$_4$+) **2**

magnesium (Mg++) calcium (Ca++) sulphur (S++) **3**

manganese (Mn++) copper (Cu++) zinc (Zn++) **4**

phosphorus (PO$_4$---) iron (Fe+++) molybdenum (Mo+++) **5**

Water-logging – more of a possibility in the lower root zone (row **5**) – makes it more difficult for elements to be taken up by the plant

rate, the soil temperature should be at least 16.6C. This is, of course, related to the aeration of the compost and to the ease with which warm air can pass in and out of it.

Roots need oxygen from the air for respiration and equally the carbon dioxide, which they exude as a by-product of this, must be able to escape back into the glasshouse atmosphere where it has a useful effect.

The primary physical requirement of a good potting compost is therefore, the ability to provide both adequate water and nutrients together with optimum gaseous exchange in close proximity to all the active root hairs. This is a very exacting requirement and many proprietary composts fall far short of the ideal. Most large pot chrysanthemum growers not only check compost analysis frequently but have a close liaison with their compost suppliers so that the standard of potting substrates is generally high.

Nutrients

For the best growth at each stage of the plant's life cycle a certain combination of the major and minor elements of nutrition is required. Feeding is dealt with in detail in chapter 3 but the main elements of chrysanthemum nutrition are: nitrogen, phosphorus, potassium, magnesium, sulphur, calcium, manganese, boron, copper, iron, zinc and molybdenum.

It is very important to realise that the roots of the plant take up these elements of nutrition selectively with little correlation with the plant's actual requirement for growth. Good composts containing all of the essential nutrients may be used but chrysanthemum plants will not necessarily take up these nutrients in the proportion in which they are mixed in the compost.

In fact the elements of nutrition can be divided into five groups according to the ease with which the plant roots will take them up from the substrate by osmosis – see panel (page 21).

The healthier the roots, the more likely it is that they are able to take up some of the elements which are difficult to reach such as phosphorus and iron. If conditions in the compost, such as waterlogging, lead to a lack of aeration and thus to root loss or inactivity, the plants will immediately run short of phosphorus and iron. In these conditions especially high levels of potassium, sodium and ammonium nitrogen which are easily taken up even by sick roots will seriously limit the plant's uptake of magnesium, calcium and sulphur.

Low root temperatures will also affect a plant's ability to take up nutrients such as phosphorus and sulphur.

Since plant proteins are based on nitrogen, sulphur and phosphorus it is, therefore, essential to maintain a healthy root system in order to provide the plants with the required balance of these elements. Similarly chlorophyll production depends on magnesium and iron, both of which can be blocked from the roots quite easily by excess potassium and other nutrients and, when roots are sick, chlorosis follows almost immediately.

Much has been learned about nutrition in recent years and the knowledge is being put to good use. In order to make sure that nutrition is correct it is wise, as stated, to send routine samples for analysis. A good peat compost analysis is given on page 29. Sometimes compost manufacturers use excess potassium and upwards of 400 ppm K will upset the availability of other nutrients to the plant's roots.

Four weeks after planting an analysis of plant sap – taken from a young, mature leaf sample – will show what the plants are actually taking up and using for growth. Any imbalance of nutrient in the plant can then be made good by either adjusting the liquid feed or, in the case of iron or magnesium deficiency for instance, by foliar feeding. This latter method may be the only effective   one if calcium and potassium levels in the plant are too high. In this way the nutrition requirements of the crop can be monitored and information regarding the best plant sap analysis for different periods of the year can be noted and used as models for the future. The important point is that leaf symptoms (except those caused by pests and diseases) are usually a sign of a root malfunction or indicate the balance of nutrients in the soil.

The maxim should be to keep the roots healthy and the rest of the plant will tend to look after itself.

3 Production

Daylength. Environment. Rooting. Cuttings management. Crop management. Bench types and watering systems. Nutrition. Height control. Variety choice. Marketing stage. Programmes.

Pot chrysanthemum grown year round enjoy one big advantage over the year-round cut flower crop. Although prices tend to fluctuate rather too much to inspire complete confidence in the crop, it is less susceptible to import competition. For this reason there is more stability in the production of pot chrysanthemums (in the UK at least) provided cropping is not overdone at certain times of the year. There is also a continuing process of increasing variety range and thus consumer demand.

Year-round pot chrysanthemums are potentially more profitable than cut flower crops but the capital investment required is far greater. In addition two of the three major production costs – labour and cuttings – are much higher as are marketing costs.

One significant difference is production time. Unrooted cuttings to finished product can, at certain times of the year, take only nine weeks. For this reason husbandry techniques must be carried out with extreme care and precision to avoid failure. There is no time to correct a major mistake in any given crop.

DAYLENGTH

Pot chrysanthemums require few long-days prior to short-day treatments so that a very small percentage of the cropping area need be equipped with night-break lighting. Long-days are normally required for the rooting period (10 days to two weeks) and occasionally for certain varieties for a further one or two weeks, in poor light conditions or prior to the winter crop.

Because plants are at close spacing during this period the lit area is only 6 or 7% of the total production area. Because plants are normally grown five to a pot and uniformity of flowering is an essential ingredient of quality, it is particularly important to use sufficient night-break lighting to prevent premature budding. This is also important for growers who are producing their own cuttings and the rule is to over-light rather than run any risk of budding on stock plants due to long night induction.

It should also be mentioned that the Princess Anne family produce only 20 or 21 leaves in long days before the long-day leaf bud is initiated at the apex of the shoot. In good growing conditions these leaves are produced at the rate of one per day. Bearing in mind that there are six leaves in the axillary bud left on the stock plant at the time of taking the cutting, there is a period of only two weeks or so before the next flush of cuttings will be producing long-day buds. Cuttings must therefore be removed very regularly from stock plants to avoid premature budding in long days.

Short-day control is equally important because of the nature of the crop. One or two delayed flowering stems in a cut flower crop due to shafts of light penetrating the black-out material may be cut late and will probably not be wasted. In a pot plant crop, uneven flowering, caused by inefficient blacking-out will spoil the crop and reduce income by a far greater extent.

Supplementary light

It has been known for some years (since the work of Cockshull and Hughes at Reading University in the late 1960's) that supplementary light given to pot chrysanthemums during the first two weeks of short days both improves flowering response and leads to greater uniformity of flowering in individual pot plants.

Light levels were raised from 0.63MJ/sq m /day (the daily average in glasshouses in southern England in mid-winter) to 1.25MJ/sq m /day for the two week period. Further work in practice showed that better plants could be produced in this way but the costs of installation and running costs of lamps were not covered by sufficient extra return from the markets. The situation has now changed somewhat for the better.

There is now a definite higher mark-up for good, rather than average, pots and supplementary lighting has become a worthwhile investment for winter and early spring production.

Work in recent winters at Efford EHS has explored a wider range of supplementary light treatments. Two of the most successful have been the use of 400W high pressure sodium (SON/T) lamps to supply 5,000 lux for the first three short-day weeks and others to supply 2,000 lux from the start of short days to the end of the crop.

The use of the latter treatment is more expensive than using 5,000 lux for three weeks but overall is probably the option most growers will favour. With Princess Anne varieties the 5,000 lux, three short-day week treatment reduced flowering time by one week. The 2,000 lux throughout treatment not only reduced flowering time by six days but induced more compact plants with greener leaves.

Shorter, faster varieties, such as Surf, Boaldi etc but which are not sufficiently vigorous for winter production without supplementary light were markedly improved in the 1991/92 winter. 5,000 lux during the first three short-day weeks improved crop time by up to four days but produced taller plants than those given 2,000 lux extra throughout short-day. This treatment also induced greater uniformity of flowering and an increased bud count.

Work in 1993/94 on single pot varieties confirmed these results and showed that use of supplementary light did not decrease shelf life.

Increase of costs due to supplementary lighting were shown to be 11.7p/pot and 14.9p/pot for the 5,000 lux treatment for three weeks and the 2,000 lux treatment throughout short-days respectively.

The Efford experiments also confirmed that the use of supplementary light during the second week of propagation is beneficial in inducing faster and more uniform crops.

A number of leading growers do, therefore, use 2,000 lux supplementary light throughout the winter pot crops from the time the plastic is removed in the propagation area until marketing.

ENVIRONMENT

Work during the 1980's at Efford EHS showed that the Princess Anne varieties can tolerate lower temperatures than some cut flower varieties. Results of trials at a range of night temperatures from 10C during the winter suggested that the temperature regime below could be implemented with little adverse effect on quality and response of the Princess Anne range.

However fewer growers now use Princess Anne varieties, preferring the faster, shorter jointed, more spreading types bred by Yoder's and Cleangro. To maximise bud set, especially in winter, these varieties have a temperature regime set at 18C day and night with ventilation at 21C.

Night temperatures

Autumn – to end February

Weeks 1 to 4 of short-days	15.0C
Week 5 onwards	13.3C

From March 1

Weeks 1 to 4 of short-days	13.3C
Week 5 onwards	10.0C

DROP treatments

During the winter of 1993/94, Efford EHS examined the effect of a temperature different (DIF) treatment on the quality of pot chrysanthemums. The treatment is perhaps better described as DROP because it represents a 6C drop in temperature from dawn for three hours.

Up to 12.5% height reduction was achieved using DROP treatments. However, as B-Nine achieves between 17.6% and 29.4 % height reduction depending on variety,

DROP treatments cannot replace growth regulators.

Further work on combinations and timing of DROP treatment, with growth regulators and spacing may well result in increased production and quality of pot plants through the winter period.

Carbon dioxide enrichment

The benefits of carbon dioxide enrichment for pot chrysanthemums are not as great as those for cut flower production but, nevertheless, are worthwhile. Results at Efford EHS show that, although quality of flowering is not markedly improved, the flowering response can be accelerated by five days. Enrichment to 1,000vpm from early November to mid-March is the correct treatment, with ventilators open above 5% enrichment should be at 500vpm.

Avoidance of uneven production in February and March caused by late flowering of some cuttings in poor light is an important factor in pot plant production. In conjunction with supplementary lighting, carbon dioxide enrichment is likely to produce more uniform and earlier flowering crops with a probable increase in quality.

Humidity

Very high humidity – up to 95% RH – can occur in pot plant programmes when combinations of solid benches with matting, CO_2 enrichment and thermal screening to conserve heat at night occur at the same time. Build up of fungal problems such as Botrytis and black rot of buds caused by physical damage followed by bacterial infection might result.

In the conditions described above, the plants continue to take up water and nutrients but the rate of transpiration is much reduced. Guttation of water and nutrients can occur and the resultant drying and crystallisation of fertilisers on leaf edges can cause damage which will be susceptible to fungal invasion. Even more seriously, the plant may become damaged internally as cells burst under water and cell sap pressure with inevitable rotting of the more vulnerable plant parts.

It is wise to allow a period of ventilation during the day to reduce humidity, to complete watering during the early hours of the day and to promote warm air circulation under the thermal screens in order to prevent excessive humidity from becoming a problem.

Husbandry

With the year-round pot plant crop, quality of unrooted cuttings is of paramount importance whether bought in from a propagator or self-produced. Uniformity in weight and leaf area of cutting is more important than actual intrinsic quality in terms of size and dry weight.

Above all the cuttings should have the ability to produce roots uniformly in good rooting conditions. In order for this to occur, the cuttings will need to contain a uniform and balanced level of nutrition in the cell sap.

ROOTING

It is very convenient to stick cuttings directly into the pots, filled with a nutritionally sound compost. This is the norm, whichever size of plant is being produced.

The usual pot size is the 14cm half-pot, with five cuttings per pot. In order to maximise potential pot plant diameter, cuttings should be inserted to a depth of no more than 15mm equidistant around the extreme edge of the pot. It is incorrect to insert cuttings 10 to 20mm inside the edge of the pot.

During sticking, diseased, damaged and uneven (either too weak or too large) cuttings are discarded. It will cost as much to grow as a good cutting but the returns will suffer if a poor cutting is introduced into the production system. Adequate watering in with a rose is essential to firm the cuttings into the compost and, if rooting under plastic sheeting is to be carried out, a final watering-in or heavy wet spray with an anti-Botrytis fungicide and a bactericide before covering is a worthwhile insurance.

B-Nine applications

During the rooting period, usually within the first seven days, an application of B-Nine is necessary to prevent stretching. This is normally at the 0.125%0 rate but varies according to variety. It is usual to allow the cuttings to regain turgidity after sticking and apply B-Nine just before dark, allowing the cuttings to remain without water application overnight. The following morning the plastic sheet is replaced or spraylines switched on again.

Rooting with plastic covering is ideal for pot chrysanthemums as it ensures that little or no nutrient is leached from the foliage during the first week. During summer conditions especially, rooting in pots under mist both leaches nutrients from cuttings and keeps the peat too moist.

After seven days, plastic covers should be removed as root primordia will be growing into the compost and can support the plants' water requirements. Occasional misting may be necessary but in ideal rooting conditions of high humidity, little watering of compost will be necessary unless high light conditions prevail.

If rooted under mist, the application of water should be carefully monitored from Day 7 to Day 14 to prevent undue stretch of plants. It is extremely important during the second week to lay the foundation of a good strong plant capable of holding three to four large flowers without bending or breaking when the pot is marketed.

COMPOST

The correct choice of compost is crucial to the success of the year-round chrysanthemum pot crop. Two main factors have to be considered apart from cost. These are the physical and chemical nature of the compost, both of which affect the roots' capability of remaining healthy and of taking up the optimum quantity of water and nutrient.

Physical requirements

In theory, a number of primary components of composts fulfil the roots' need of good aeration combined with adequate water. A well-aerated compost will facilitate root respiration and allow roots to take up more easily those elements such as iron which are unavailable in composts which do not allow for optimum root growth. Also, well-aerated composts are warmer than others ie nearer to air temperature, and roots operate more efficiently at higher rather than lower temperatures within the range of 10C to 20C.

A factor of modern production is the ease and speed by which large numbers of plants can be moved around the nursery either for spacing or marketing. Weight of compost is, therefore, another important factor, and virtually rules out composts based on large volumes of loam such as John Innes composts. However a number of proprietary brands of peat, peat/Perlite or peat/vermiculite composts are available which produce plants equally good or better than those grown in John Innes and which provide the required lightness in weight, even when pots are at field capacity after watering.

Physical components of compost can be divided into those which have a good ion exchange capacity and those which do not.

Peat is a good ion exchange medium whilst Perlite and polystyrene chips are added to composts purely for aeration purposes and have no ion exchange capacity. Vermiculite aids aeration and has some ion exchange capability. Coarse sand or gravel add weight to a compost and aid aeration.

It has, however, been found in practice that a peat with a good structure, especially young sphagnum peat, holds sufficient air even at field capacity for optimum root growth and can be used without other additives which might reduce ion exchange. At the same time, it must be stated that some peats and also some proprietary brands of all-peat compost are too fine or are ground too fine during mixing to allow optimum root growth. These peat composts may be made usable by the addition of Perlite, polystyrene or vermiculite but with added cost and reduced ion exchange capacity.

Chemical requirements

Composts for pot chrysanthemums should contain the correct combinations between the elements of nutrition, especially the main ones of N, P and K. This is important because the plants have a very short period of vegetative growth in which to develop to a sufficient size for an even breaking action following pinching and

A good balance of nutrients – mg/litre

N	P	K	Mg	S	Ca	Mn	B	Cu	Zn	Fe
225	150	200	225	175	1,500	1.5	1.3	20	40	150

EC should be about 4.0   pH should be between 5.3 and 6.0

uniform bud set across the pot. Very few proprietary brands of compost contain the ideal chemical balance and growers are tending towards mixing their own composts. A very good balance of nutrients for pot chrysanthemums at potting or sticking time is shown in the panel (page 28).

A compost which is very near to the above ideal and which was developed many years ago by Bunt as a general purpose compost is the GCRI Potting Compost 1. The original version contained 25% by volume of fine sand but if a well structured sphagnum peat is used 100%, the following fertilisers should be added per cubic metre

	kg/cu m
ammonium nitrate	0.4
superphosphate	1.5
potassium nitrate	0.75
ground limestone	2.4
Dolomite limestone	2.4
fritted trace elements (WM55)	0.375

An analysis of this compost for the three main nutrients gives the following values:

230mg/litre	N
120mg/litre	P
290mg/litre	K

Nitrogen is available both in the NH_4 form (30%) and the NO_3 form. It is known that with the ammonium ions available plants take up iron and molybdenum more readily. Another good mix, again using 100% sphagnum peat, is shown in the panel (left).

In this compost, iron and molybdenum are not used because these elements are much more readily available to the plants if supplied in the liquid feed as iron chelate and sodium molybdate.

Of course, there is a choice of fertilisers to achieve the correct proportion of nutrients in the finished compost and there is infinite scope for experimentation to provide the best compost for individual needs. In the above compost, for instance, the micronutrients could be omitted as individual chemicals and the fritted trace WM55 developed by Bunt could be insert-

Fertiliser mix for 100% spagnum peat

	kg/cu m
potassium nitrate	0.4
calcium nitrate (15.5% N)	0.325
triple superphosphate	0.25
ground rock phosphate (basic slag)	1.5
ground limestone	3.0
Dolomite limestone	2.0
magnesium sulphate	0.4

	g/cu m
borax	8
copper sulphate	50
zinc sulphate	75
manganese sulphate	10

ed. Also, a percentage of the nitrogen could be added as ammonium nitrate.

In all cases it must be remembered that the compost is only one factor and must be considered in relation to the type of bench and watering system which will affect the availability of nutrients (leaching, etc) and the environmental conditions within the compost (degree of water holding and aeration).

CUTTINGS MANAGEMENT

Because the majority of pot chrysanthemums are now direct stuck it is essential, as already mentioned, to ensure that only cuttings within a certain specification of uniformity are inserted into the pots. Beyond this there is little the grower can do to control uniformity in the cuttings except provide ideal and uniform conditions for rooting. Growers must assume that cuttings have been snapped from short shoots (ie no long-day leaf buds) and that stock plants have been fed correctly.

Where growers root pot plant cuttings in a normal bench or small container for potting on, there is more scope for grading. This entails more labour but can produce a better quality pot when a good potting compost is used. Unfortunately some of the proprietary brands of compost contain so much potassium and sulphate that salt levels are 50% higher than they should be and watery young roots on conventionally rooted cuttings are physically damaged during the first few days after potting. Those cuttings which are stuck directly into pots seem to produce roots which can cope more successfully with the high salt content in these composts.

Grading rooted cuttings is very important if there is considerable variability in the quality of the unrooted cutting. Cuttings of medium wet weight (say 1.5g) will flower three or four days earlier than very vegetative heavy cuttings (2.5g or more) and up to 10 days earlier than thin cuttings (less than 1g) in poor winter light.

A further point to bear in mind is that when pot cuttings have been produced in the UK rather than more southerly countries, growth will be softer and the base of the cutting will be more slowly lignified in cold store. Cuttings produced in the UK, especially those grown during late autumn to early spring, will need at least a week in cold-storage before being able to root at the maximum rate and even so may root more slowly than bought in cuttings. This must be allowed for in rooting time.

When grading rooted cuttings the most important factor is weight of plant which is best measured by thickness of stem and leaf area. The amount of root should also be considered. In an uneven batch of cuttings three grades of rooted cutting may be necessary for optimum results bearing in mind that all five cuttings in a 14cm pot need to perform in the same way.

CROP MANAGEMENT

The essential features are to place the plants equidistant around the edge of the pot, with the roots no deeper than they were in the rooting bench and to firm the plants only sufficiently to keep them from falling out of the pot when watering in. Plants

Left: Cuttings, stuck direct into pots, pot thick, under plastic on a warm concrete floor

Below: While still at half-spacing plants are pinched uniformly, leaving eight to 10 leaves on each shoot

Plants on the right are direct from the rooting area and are opened out to half-spacing; those on the left are one week older

Above: Pots after two weeks at half-spacing

Right: After three weeks at half-spacing plants are opened out to final spacing ready for final B-Nine spray

Below: Five weeks from rooting foliage fully covers bench area

Tools of the trade. Mobile benching, lamps and bench irrigation all serve to facilitate crop management. Supplementary light over the benches (right) ensures maximum winter quality while using the bench watering system (below) the pots take up water from the matting via permeable black polythene automatically

Growing on ebb-and-flood floors. Top: Plants from the prop area at half-spacing

Above: Watered from below in 20-minute sessions, foliage soon covers the floor area

Left: Plants at half-spacing using diagonal pattern for maximum efficiency

A reliable filter like this (left), together with reliable pump are necessary for the level of water and feed control needed by the crop

Above left:Good pots can also be grown direct on the greenhouse floor provided the soil has been levelled, firmed and covered by matting
Above right: Bright Golden Anne almost ready for market

Young stock plants (left) pinched to provide the first flush of cuttings

A batch of stock plants (below) with the first cuttings ready to take. The large ones will be taken first, the smaller one left two days to mautre

Cuttings ready to take from short shoots

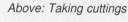

Above: Taking cuttings

These shoots (left) are too long for cuttings and may produce premature buds; the long-day leaf bud (below) resulted from a cutting taken from a very long shoot on the stock plant

Bottom: The ideal; uniform cuttings treated with rooting powder

Trays of cuttings in pots (right) set out on a warm concrete floor and covered with milk white plastic

Left: The author striking cuttings, five to a 13cm pot to produce the uniformly spaced arrangement (below)

Left: Newly struck pots ready for transfer to the production area; note the label for batch identification purposes

Planting up a 13cm pot

5 cuttings (3 shown) are spaced equidistant around the circumferance, angled outwards about 45 deg

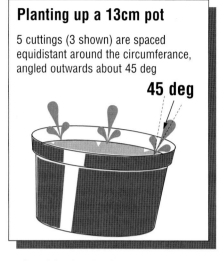

45 deg

angled at 45 deg to the upright will eventually produce a larger plant than those planted almost upright. This is one of the advantages of potting rooted cuttings compared with direct sticking unrooted cuttings.

Daylength control and pinching

The ideal pot chrysanthemum in a 14cm pot should measure at least 30cm in diameter and the height of the plant, including the pot, should be no more than 30cm. To achieve this, the two most important factors, apart from chemical growth regulation, are the number of long days from sticking and the timing and nature of the pinch.

Careful selection by breeders has, over the last 10 years, resulted in the average height of chrysanthemum pot plants being reduced and also in a smaller difference between the tallest and shortest varieties. Instead of tall (some very tall), medium and short, we now have, in recently introduced varieties, medium/tall, medium and medium/short. The height of most these new varieties can be controlled by the use of B-Nine alone (but see page 47).

The panel (right) lists response groups of some of the major pot varieties under the new height categories. The direct sticking of cuttings into fully fertilised compost will, if the rooting environment is ideal, result in much faster growth compared with cuttings rooted

Varieties by height category

| Habit | Response group | | |
	8 week	8 $^1/2$ week	9 week
MEDIUM/TALL	Tangerine Time	Bi-Time	Orange Time
		Lady Time	Davis
MEDIUM	Song Time	Boaldi	Tempo
	Surf	Ice Time	
	Yellow	Firetime	
	Pele	Yellow Diamond	
	Tara	Charm	
		Regal About Time	
		White Blush	
MEDIUM/ SMALL	Jewel Time	Dream Time	Pico

Long-day regime

	Sticking period	Weeks of long-days
Tall varieties	Wk 40 – Wk 8	1
	Wk 9 – Wk 39	0
Medium varieties	Wk 40 – Wk 8	2
	Wk 9 – Wk 39	1

in unfertilised benches and then potted on. There is, of course, no potting check with the former practice.

Long-day schedules

The schedules given for long-day requirement in previous publications (eg 'Chrysanthemums – year round growing' by Machin and Scopes, Blandford Press 1978 page 126) for potting rooted cuttings can now be much simplified. Allow two weeks of long-days for rooting. Space into intermediate spacing and thereafter follow the long-day regime in the panel (left).

Growers of short varieties such as Surf in 9 or 14cm pots should allow a further week of long days for each period.

The above schedules relate to southern England and extra long days, especially in winter, will be needed in Midland and northern areas.

To achieve the correct balance of growth, ie neither too tall with too few breaks, nor too short with uneven breaking, the timing of the pinch relative to the start of short days is important.

In good light conditions a pinch made 10 to 14 days following the start of short days is ideal. In poor light, or when growth is less rapid for any reason, pinching after about 18 short days or even, in extreme cases, 21 short days is more correct.

Generally an early pinch leads to extra height and vice versa, but the amount of growth removed is also an important factor where height and uniformity is concerned. For instance, it is possible with high quality, uniform plants to leave pinching for 18 to 21 days after short days begin and then to pinch back to eight leaves provided that internodes are sufficiently short following correct chemical regulation. With this method there will be relatively few axillary buds to remove at disbudding time, an important labour saving on the Princess Anne varieties.

The actual pinch should always be made into soft growth leaving behind at least three leaves within a length of 15mm of stem at the top of the plant. Total leaf number remaining should be from seven to nine.

Pinching is the final operation which can influence the uniformity of the plant and tall cuttings must be pinched back harder to conform with the majority. Small cuttings can be pinched lightly so final leaf number is uniform on all plants. At least in this way final height, if not flowering response, will be uniform across the pot.

Spacing

Plants should be spaced as they grow but in practice only three spacings are necessary to achieve the twin objectives of labour saving and high quality pots.

Spacing layouts

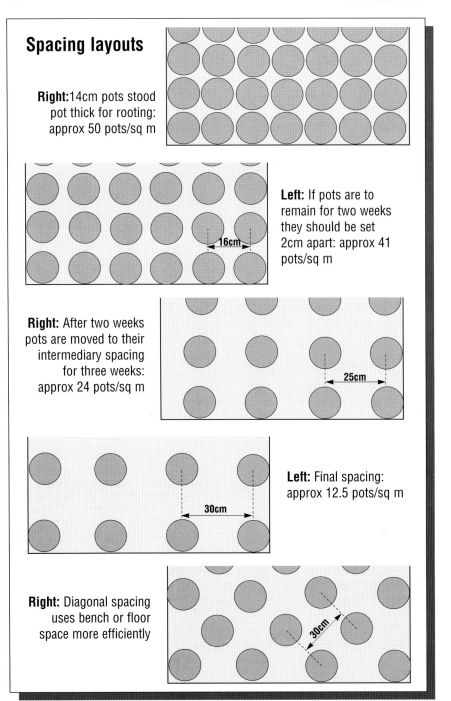

Right:14cm pots stood pot thick for rooting: approx 50 pots/sq m

Left: If pots are to remain for two weeks they should be set 2cm apart: approx 41 pots/sq m

16cm

Right: After two weeks pots are moved to their intermediary spacing for three weeks: approx 24 pots/sq m

25cm

Left: Final spacing: approx 12.5 pots/sq m

30cm

Right: Diagonal spacing uses bench or floor space more efficiently

30cm

Plants in 14cm pots containing five cuttings can be placed pot thick for rooting, but, if they are to remain for two weeks, a 2cm gap should be left between pots to allow for full leaf expansion and to avoid stretching. This allows 41 pots/sq m.

After two weeks, plants can be moved to intermediate spacing for three weeks during which time they will be pinched. This spacing can be 25 x 25cm which allows 24 pots/sq m .

Final spacing is approximately 30 x 30cm or slightly less for the shortest varieties which is about 12.5 pots/sq m.

It should be remembered that diagonal spacing allows the plant to make full use of all growing area compared with square spacing with no loss in production. Where benches are mobile the pots are spaced in such a way that when benches are tight together there are no empty spaces on the benches. For ease of movement pots may be rooted in polystyrene trays. Spacing areas should always be considered relative to the organisation of the programme.

Disbudding
Large flowered varieties such as the Princess Anne range generally produce better returns if disbudded. Other varieties may be left with lateral buds without detracting from quality. Indeed if marketing is carefully timed to allow for eventual development of lateral buds the shelf life of the pot plant is considerably increased.

BENCH TYPES AND WATERING
Early systems of static wooden slatted benches with hose watering had by 1970 given way to more sophisticated methods of benching and watering. There are three main types of benching system. Most efficient pot plant programmes use mobile bench systems although some growers are opting for laser-levelled concrete floor systems.

Open structured benching
Benching constructed with a metal mesh base and equipped with a drip nozzle for each pot at final spacing, developed at a time when one path served five mobile benches which were confined to a given area. Later and current designs – where benches move the whole length of the house from final spacing to marketing (and which utilise more than 90% of the growing area) – also use an open mesh base.

The advantage of this type of benching is that full air circulation is possible and uniform temperature control is relatively easy. Conditions in winter are ideal as a very high humidity around each plant is easy to avoid especially with low level heating pipes.

The main disadvantage is that, as uniformity of crop depends on uniformity of water and nutrient supply, drip nozzle systems need to be overhauled very frequently to avoid blocking by chemicals such as calcium phosphate etc. As the watering system ages, the uniformity of cropping tends to fall away.

Capillary problems

There are three major problems connected with the use of capillary matting in a pot chrysanthemum bench system. To combat these problems 5cm gaps should be left between benches while watering should be done early in the day to encourage lower humidity as night approaches.

Algae control
After three months' use the surface of the mat will become covered with algae which reduces its efficiency regarding capillary action. The material must be cleaned by brushing when dry, by rolling and steam sterilising between crops, by steaming in situ or by treating with algaecides. All these systems add to the cost of the programme and none is completely effective.

Salt concentrattion
There is no leaching action on capillary matting as with plants watered from above. In a pot chrysanthemum crop the high rates of liquid fertiliser quickly lead to high salt concentrations in the matting. This can scorch roots and seriously restrict growth. In conditions of high humidity and a high rate of water and nutrient uptake, there is even evidence that serious leaf scorch and other damage can occur, particularly on excessively salty patches of matting.

It is, therefore, important to squeeze the matting daily and check the EC of the leachate. Salt concentrations of liquid feeds are generally between EC figures of 1.8 and 2.5 (EC of 2.5 = CF 25= 2,500 micro-Siemens) and the salt concentrations of liquid feeds should not be allowed to exceed this. Daily leachings with clear water are often necessary in summer. The problem can be avoided by using a feed rate 30% lower than a drip watering open bench system.

Winter management
Solid benches, either matting covered or for flood watering, have potential winter management problems connected with atmosphere control. Solid benches provide good insulation and, where heating pipes are below the benches, control of fungal and bacterial diseases may prove difficult, especially when the area of air circulation is reduced by the use of a thermal screen. High humidity problems can be accentuated by the use of carbon dioxide enrichment.

Another disadvantage is that solid benches need to be provided for the intermediate spacing area (and rooting area if in the same glasshouse) so that higher humidity levels can be maintained around the youngest plants. Nevertheless, this system has proved very adequate and continues to produce high quality pots efficiently.

Solid benches

Benches with solid bases and capillary matting or flood bench watering systems are invariably constructed of light alloy, one type being made 'solid' by the use of polystyrene sheets covered with a plastic sheet and a layer of matting. The matting is kept moist by drip nozzle system or small bore plastic tube with holes at intervals.

Compared with the open mesh bench method management tends to be more difficult relative to water and nutrient uptake. Flood benches are more expensive since they have to be water tight and are heavier than benches constructed for matting. They have the advantage of a more positive watering system with the plants in a less humid atmosphere between waterings.

Both of these bench types are too heavy to move the whole length of the house for transportation to the start of the programme again following marketing. Some floor area is, therefore, lost compared with open mesh systems since about one in five benches is static.

Trough systems

Ideally a pot chrysanthemum programme should have solid benches for flowering from April to September and open mesh benches for the rest of the year. A compromise solution was offered with the development of the trough system. This system comprises a series of travelling solid benches each one-pot wide. These are capable of travelling the whole length of the house to be returned to the potting area after marketing. Water and feed is supplied to each trough and plants takes up the feed from the base so that careful monitoring of feed strength is again important.

However because the troughs allow an infinite number of pot spacing configurations the grower has far greater control over the plant environment at each stage than than with either large solid benches or open mesh benches. Troughs can be close together at the beginning of the crop and opened out weekly if necessary as they move down the house.

In additon, the pots themselves need not be moved again after they enter the system from the rooting area, saving labour. This system is expensive to install but appears to combine the best in environmental control and labour saving techniques.

Concrete floors

The most modern method of pot plant production returns crop management to the glasshouse floor. The plants, at intermediate or final spacing, are set out on laser-levelled concrete flooring which incorporates both heating pipes and ebb and flood watering. The latter enables plants to be watered periodically by flooding the floor to a depth of several centimetres for an appropriate time to allow the pots to fill to field capacity. The floor is then drained and the liquid feed solution re-circulated by means of a pump ready for the next watering.

Regular analyses are carried out and the elements of nutrition adjusted as necessary. Needless to say, installation is expensive because the floor level has to be perfect and the fall to allow drainage should be correct almost to a millimetre. However, there is no problem with high humidity with this system and it is the most efficient of all for labour-saving and ease of movement of plants especially if mechanised handling are used for placing, spacing and collecting pots.

NUTRITION

The ideal starting point for nutrient proportions in potting composts was given on page 28. Ideally all growers should check their own mixing procedures by routine analyses at given intervals. Also, where proprietary brands of compost are bought in, it is always wise to have an analysis done to check nutrient balance, salt concentration and uniformity between different batches before the crop is planted. This is particularly important before potting for a special market such as Mother's Day or Christmas.

When roots are damaged due to excessive salts or badly mixed composts there is no time allowed in the growing schedule for regrowth and recovery. Crops will merely flower late and unevenly, a situation avoided by pre-knowledge of the nutrient status of the compost.

Generally, apart from nitrogen and potassium, sufficient nutrient for much of the crop growth should be available in the compost (with the exception of iron and molybdenum in the compost formulation given on page 29). As soon as roots are formed in direct stuck crops or two days after potting rooted cuttings, the liquid feed should commence.

The proportions of K_2O will vary with the season of production and the amount of feed will vary with the variety and the system of production, remembering that on benches with capillary matting feed should be only 70% of normal concentration. However a feed of 300mg/litre N and 200mg/litre K_2O supplied with each watering from the start of short days will be a good basis to work from. The feed should be diluted by up to 50% when watering increases during high light, high temperature periods.

HEIGHT CONTROL

Height control of pot chrysanthemums cannot be achieved by daylength control and pinching techniques alone. A combination of a growth regulator in the compost with further growth regulation by overhead spraying during rooting and up to appearance of buds is often necessary.

The degree of regulation will depend mainly on variety, season of production and type of peat used in the compost.

Rates of Phosphon* for all-peat composts

Variety type	Flowering period	
	May–October	November–April
Regal Anne	0.75kg/cu m	0.45kg/cu m
Bright Golden Anne	0.60kg/cu m	0.30kg/cu m

* 1.5 granulet

Phosfon. The panel is a guide to Princess Anne varieties of differing vigour for the use of Phosfon 1.5 granulet in a mixture of sphagnum and sedge peats. Bright Golden Anne is less vigorous than Regal Anne. Some young sphagnum peats require no Phosfon, even during summer, while plants in an all sedge peat compost may require more than the rates given to achieve height control. Phosfon 1.5 granulet is a useful regulant because it has a continuing effect on growth from the time the roots emerge and come into contact with it. It does, however, have to be mixed in the compost and causes about four days flowering delay compared with plants controlled only with B-Nine. It is possible to arrange with some manufacturers of compost, for Phosfon to be incorporated at mixing time. However with the greatly increasing use of varieties other than the tall Princess Annes, there is now much less need for Phosfon and control can be acheived by the use of B-nine alone.

B-Nine. B-Nine (daminozide) contains 85% active ingredient as a wettable powder and is used as a foliar spray. It is applied during rooting and, if Phosfon is incorporated into the compost, once again when breaks are 10 to 15 mm long following pinching.

During winter flowering height control can be achieved by the use of B-Nine alone but up to four applications may be necessary. It is impossible to give precise instructions for each variety in each compost in each production location but the table on page 47 gives some guidance for each height category. Adjustments can then be made in the light of experience.

Dilution rates vary from 0.0132% up to 0.375%. A dilution rate of 0.125% can be achieved by adding 50g of B-Nine to 34 litres of water.

VARIETY CHOICE

For some years the market has demanded higher quality in pot chrysanthemums, returning premium prices for good quality uniform pots marketed at the correct stage of growth compared with average or poor material. There is every incentive, therefore, to make use of all aids to good production, such as supplementary lighting and carbon dioxide enrichment, and to make careful choices of varieties for each season of the year.

Until recently the Princess Anne family dominated the market (up to 90%) round

How much B-Nine?
The strength of B-Nine in solution

	Flowering period			
	May to October		November to April	
	With Phosphon	Without Phosphon	With Phosphon	Without Phosphon
Regal Anne V/T				
2 days after sticking	0.625%	0.125%	0.625%	0.125%
14 days after sticking	—	0.125%	—	0.125%
7 days after SD's commence	—	0.25%	—	—
When breaks are 10–15mm long	0.375%	0.5%	0.25%	0.375%
Bright Golden Anne T				
2 days after sticking	0.625%	0.125%	0.625%	0.125%
14 days after sticking	—	0.0625%	—	0.0625%
7 days after SD's commence	—	0.125%	—	—
When breaks are 10–15mm long	0.25%	0.375%	0.185%	0.25%
Davis M/T				
2 days after sticking	0.0312%	0.0625%	0.0312%	0.0625%
14 days after sticking	—	0.0312%	—	0.0312%
7 days after SD's commence	—	0.0625%	—	—
When breaks are 10–15mm long	0.125%	0.25%	0.0625%	0.125%
Surf M				
2 days after sticking	0.312%	0.0625%	0.0312%	0.0625%
14 days after sticking	—	0.0312%	—	0.0312%
7 days after SD's commence	—	0.0312%	—	—
When breaks are 10–15mm long	0.0625%	0.125%	0.0312%	0.0625%
Dreamtime M/S				
2 days after sticking	—	—	—	—
14 days after sticking	—	0.0132	—	0.0312
7 days after SD's commence	—	—	—	—
When braks are 10-15 mm long	—	0.0625	—	0.0312

SD= short-days VT= very tall T=tall M/T= medium tall M= medium M/S= medium short the year. Now not only is there a movement towards an increasing range of types, eg singles, anemones and quills, particularly during the period April to October, but the Princess Anne range have been largely superseded by shorter, earlier-flowering decoratives mainly bred by Yoder Bros Inc and Cleangro Ltd. Many of these newer types cannot yet be produced up to minimum quality level during the winter months without supplementary light as many were bred in the USA, but there is an increasing number of new varieties being bred for north European conditions round the year.

At the time of writing the varieties which can be produced from January to March are mainly decorative varieties (table overleaf) although some of the single flowered types can be flowered for Christmas if given at least two weeks of long days from potting (three or four weeks long days from direct sticking).

Princess Anne family

Princess Annes are still grown by some specialist producers at five plants in a pot but are decreasing in importance. A good range

Variety choice

DECORATIVES

	Weeks of SD's before marketing	Height category
White varieties		
Boaldi*	$8^1/_2$	medium
Ice Time*	$8^1/_2$	medium
Jewel Time	8	medium/short
Song time	8	medium
Story Time	8	medium
Surf*	8	medium
White Diamond	$8^1/_2$	medium
White Disney Time	8	medium/tall
Yellow varieties		
Bright Golden Anne	10	tall
Dark Yellow Boaldi*	$8^1/_2$	medium
Fine Time	9	medium
Fire Time*	$8^1/_2$	medium
Sunny Time	$8^1/_2$	medium/short
Surfine	$8^1/_2$	medium
Yellow About Time	$8^1/_2$	medium
Yellow Diamond*	$8^1/_2$	medium
Yellow Jewel Time	8	medium/short
Yuba	$8^1/_2$	medium
Pink varieties		
About Time	$8^1/_2$	medium
Charm*	$8^1/_2$	medium
Delano	$8^1/_2$	medium
Disney Time	8	medium/tall
Lady Time	$8^1/_2$	medium/tall
Proud Princess Anne	10	tall
Regal About Time*	$8^1/_2$	medium
Tempo*	9	medium
Red/Bronze varieties		
Gay Anne	10	tall
Orange About Time	$8^1/_2$	medium
Red About Time	$8^1/_2$	medium
Red Delano*	$8^1/_2$	medium
Tangerine Time	8	medium/tall

* Illustrated on pages 56 to 62

of form and colour is available but each mutation is different in certain aspects of growth. Regal, Purple and Crimson Anne are the tallest of the family with slightly smaller, paler leaves than the others. Bright Golden Anne and Proud Anne are shorter and stockier whilst Gay Anne has the latest flowering response.

In order to produce a uniform box of six plants containing four of the above family for a given market eg Christmas, different chemical regulation treatments and different dates for commencement of short days will be necessary. If Bright Golden Anne is taken as average in response time, then Crimson and Regal Anne will have to commence short-day treatment three days later and Gay Anne three days earlier to produce flowering plants at the same stage of development in the winter months.

Decorative types

During the period October to March it appears that the best colour requirements per box of six Annes is:

Three yellow
(at least two Bright
    Golden Anne)
One pink
One red or purple
One bronze

Variety choice

SINGLES

	Weeks of SD's before marketing	Height category
White varieties		
Dance	9	medium
Denver	$8^1/_2$	medium
Shasta	8	medium
White Blush*	$8^1/_2$	medium
Yellow varieties		
Miramar	$8^1/_2$	medium
Nugget Time	$8^1/_2$	medium
Yellow Dana	9	medium
Yellow Tan*	8	medium
Pink varieties		
Blush	$8^1/_2$	medium
Davis	9	medium/tall
Light Davis*	9	medium/tall
Lively Time	9	medium/tall
Monteray	9	medium
Splendor	9	medium
Velvet Time	8	medium
Red/Bronze varieties		
Dark Tan	8	medium
Lucido	9	medium
Orange Davis*	9	medium/tall
Pelee*	8	medium
Rage	9	medium/tall

These singles should not be flowered from January to mid-March unless supplementary light is available for crop production

*Illustrated on pages 56 to 62

Variety choice

ANEMONES/SPOONS

	Weeks of SD's before marketing	Height category
White varieties		
Bi-Time	8^1/$_2$	medium/tall
Dream Time*	8^1/$_2$	medium/short
Merced	8	medium
Spears	9	medium
Tara*	8	medium
Yellow varieties		
Forge	9	medium
Midas Time	8^1/$_2$	medium/short
Pico*	9	medium/short
Yellow Merced	8	medium
Pink varieties		
Dark Akira	8^1/$_2$	medium
Lucky Time	9	medium/tall
Purple Lucky Time	9	medium/tall
Red/bronze varieties		
Jasper	8^1/$_2$	medium

These varieties should not be flowered from January to mid-March unless supplementary light is available for crop production
*Illustrated on pages 56 to 62

During the remainder of the year, slightly more pink and less yellow is a consideration and the box of six Annes may be made up as:

Two yellow
(both Bright Golden
  Anne)
Two pink
(one dark and one paler
  pink)
One purple or red
One bronze

Medium flowered decoratives

There is an increasing and very beautiful range of varieties with a shorter more compact habit but with smaller flowers than the Princess Anne family. They have been bred in the USA and in southern England and are much easier to grow than the Princess Anne family - requiring less growth regulation and providing many more flowers per pot. Because they are less vigorous, more long days are required and supplementary light during the winter improves quality.

Singles, anemones and quills

There is now a good range of these varieties available for flowering from late spring to autumn but they can only be grown in winter with supplementary light. Since white is more acceptable to markets in single, anemone or quill forms compared with decoratives, a good balance of colour in a box of six is:

One white
Two yellow
(one medium and one deep shade)
One pink
One purple or red
One bronze

Varieties for small pots

There has never been a great demand for chrysanthemums in pots in sizes other than 14cm in the UK. There is a limited demand for single plants in 9cm pots for which the variety Popsie and its sports were developed. The newer, short decoratives and all the singles, anemones and quills listed are all suitable for production as single plants in pots.

Stage for marketing

The trade for pot chrysanthemums has been significantly damaged in the past due to marketing plants at too early a stage of development. The best place for growth of the plant during the later stages of its life cycle is the glasshouse with full light conditions. Pots which are marketed in tight bud will never develop sufficiently in the shop or home. The correct stage of development of a disbudded plant in a 14cm pot for marketing is as follows:

April–October
    At least 5 flowers half-developed with colour showing on all other buds

November–March
    At least 5 flowers three-quarters developed (ie with some petals extended to almost full length) with colour showing on all other buds

PROGRAMMES

The pot chrysanthemum programme needs careful planning for maximum production. In a single E/W widespan house, a good plan is to divide the area equally. At each end of the house sufficient E/W static benching is built to house the rooting and intermediate spaced plants needed to fill one side of the main part of the house which is filled with mobile N/S benches which travel the length of the house.

Maturing plants travel in opposite directions in the main area until they are ready to be marketed at each end of the house. About 90% of the floor area is utilised.

The number of plants to pot each week to fill both the flowering area at all times and to avoid overcrowding when response slows in poor light needs careful calculation. The table (overleaf) gives an indication of the total number of weeks for cropping at different periods of the year for a typical Princess Anne programme in southern England without supplementary lighting.

If it is assumed that 90% of the floor area of an 0.4ha production area can be utilised for pot production (ie 3,642sq m) the calculations for output are :

Rooting   2 weeks at 0.026sq m/pot/week = 0.052sq m
Intermediate spacing 3 weeks at 0.46sq m/pot/week = 0.138sq m
Total   = 0.190sq m

Cropping schedule

Period	Flowering weeks	No. of weeks	Weeks at final spacing	Total cropping time (weeks)
1	27–38	12	6	9
2	39–45 & 22–36	12	7	10
3	46–51 & 18–21	10	8	11
4	52–5 & 14–17	10	9	12
5	6–13	8	10	13

The number of weeks at final spacing now has to be taken into account assuming an area of 0.102sq m/pot/week. Production for each period can now be calculated as follows:

No. of pots/week for each production period = bench area (3,642sq m) divided by total growing area required for each pot during each period

More responsive varieties than Princess Anne (ie all 8 to 9 week types) will take less time at final spacing but will need more long days at certain times. They can also be held for longer at intermediate spacing. However the calculations for prodution at each period of the year to give total production can be made as in the sample for the Princess Anne family given below.

Period	Total growing area for each pot	Pots per week	No of weeks of production	Total No of pots
1	0.802sq m	4,541	12	54,492
2	0.904sq m	4,029	12	48,348
3	0.1006sq m	3,620	10	36,200
4	0.108sq m	3,287	10	32,870
5	0.210sq m	3,101	8	24,808
			Total for year	196,718

4 Stock & cuttings

Plant health. Stock production. Watering and lighting. Stock nutrition. Taking cuttings. Cuttings treatment. Stock planning.

Year-round production of pot chrysanthemums began in the UK in 1957. Until the early 1960's all cuttings required for these programmes were raised in Sussex. It was during this period that the English chrysanthemum industry really became established and it quickly became apparent that winter light levels reduced the production rate of cuttings from stock plants and much more area had to be allocated for stock purposes from October to February. This was the main reason why commercial propagators moved south to areas where production factors remained fairly constant.

At about the same time labour in Malta and Gran Canaria was cheap, a factor which is much less significant now. There has never been any doubt that stock plants and cuttings could not be produced in the south of England to the performance level required for good flower production. Economic factors alone led propagators in the 1970's to favour more southern latitudes and in recent years cuttings have been imported to Europe from as far as South Africa, Brazil and Costa Rica.

To buy in or not?

The cost of unrooted cuttings accounts for a substantial part of total production costs. For an average pot chrysanthemum programme the cuttings bill is approximately £31,000 an acre. For this reason some growers in northern Europe still do produce their own cuttings, at least for part of the year and make a significant saving in the process. Whether or not a grower should contemplate cuttings production requires careful consideration.

There is a lot to be said for securing a regular supply of cuttings from a commercial propagator. The pot chrysanthemum grower can generally rely on good service and can devote his entire energy to growing and selling his plants.

However keeping your own stock plants and taking your own cuttings does have advantages. The potential cost saving is between 33 and 50% of the cost of buying in against which has to be set the extra management requirement for the stock house and most growers do not realise that stock management is more intricate and difficult than flower production management.

PLANT HEALTH

All the major diseases and some of the major pests of the year-round chrysanthemum crop have been imported to the UK from all parts of the chrysanthemum-growing world.

In the early days of production, stunt viroid and aspermy virus came in with the American spray varieties. Ray blight originated in Florida and was likewise imported from the USA in the 1960's.

White rust went from Japan to the USA and to Europe and it is from Europe that the British industry is now striving to keep it at bay. The latest serious pest to hit the UK in this way is the western flower thrips, *Frankliniella occidentalis*.

The caterpillar pest *Spodoptera littoralis* (Mediterranean climbing cutworm) and the very damaging leafminer, *Liriomyza trifolii*, are just two examples of notifiable pests which the UK at least is still striving to prevent from becoming endemic but which are imported on bought-in cuttings.

But millions of cuttings come into the UK every week from many parts of the world. However efficient the commercial propagators' plant health precautions are – and they have been generally excellent for many years – pests and diseases will continue to be imported.

Growers risk losing several weeks' production if serious outbreaks of white rust occur and on top of this revenue loss, there is the high costs of control.

Reliability of production

A grower who buys small amounts of tested and disease-free mother plants from a very reliable source once a year and who then builds up this stock to provide all his cuttings is in an extremely safe position regarding pests and diseases. His crops will probably suffer from all the regular problems such as red spider mite, aphids, thrips, botrytis and rhizoctonia, but his nursery should at least escape the more serious pests and diseases.

Assuming that stock has been planned correctly and all cuttings removed from the stock when ready, cuttings production is very reliable at any time of the year.

Provided cold storage facilities are available there will be an uninterrupted supply of cuttings available for the programme.

None of the problems that beset the commercial propagators from time to time – such as damage to cuttings due to overheating at airports, loss of cuttings during despatch and transport problems – will affect the self-propagator.

Above: Leafminer Liriomyza huidobrensis

Top right: Another leafminer, Phytomyza syngenisiae (picture courtesty Horticulture Research International

Right: Aphis gossypii

Above: Damage by Thrips Frankliniella. Machines like the 'Wanjet' (far right) offer an effective means of applying pesticides at low volume but it must be used in with fans like this (right)

1. Light Davis
2. Pelee
3. Boaldi
4. Surf

1. Dark Akira
2. Orange Davis
3. Dark Yellow Boaldi
4. White Blush

1. Red Delano
2. Tempo
3. Song Time
4. Fire Time

1. Dream Time
2. Regal About Time
3. Jewel Time
4. Ice Time

59

Opposite top: Charm

Opposite bottom: Tara

Yellow Tan (above) and Pico (right)

Yellow Diamond, one of Yoder Toddington's most promising new varieties

Quality of production

The quality of unrooted cuttings is the key to success of the year-round pro-gramme. The quality must also be uniform within each variety as uniformly high quality cuttings are of paramount importance. No one is more aware of this than the commercial propagators and every effort is made by them to ensure high standards.

Generally commercial propagators employ hundreds of staff and the complexity of management control is such that, compared with a 0.2ha (half-acre) block of stock with one supervisor and three or four cutting takers, quality control to the highest standard is extremely difficult. The self-producer of cuttings should, there-fore, be able to reach the high standards required more easily than the commercial propagator, but this will depend entirely on the effort put into good stock plant management. It follows that while the quality of unrooted cuttings can be improved by a careful grower, a self-producer who is merely trying to cut costs without putting in the management time required will produce inferior cuttings than he could buy in from a commercial propagator.

Stock and cuttings production requires more management skill than growing the flower crops and if the grower is not prepared to plan and grow stock to the high-est standard, he would be well advised not to consider it.

Nutrition

Nutrition is extremely important for all stages of year-round chrysanthemum pro-duction, but stock plants, because they are always in a vegetative state, require dif-ferent nutrition regimes from the flowering crop. Not all commercial propagators fully realise the importance of stock plant nutrition and this is another aspect where the careful stock producer can improve on general commercial quality.

Special aspects of stock production

Many of the husbandry techniques – preparation, sterilisation and planting – described in chapter 3 apply equally to stock production although, if anything, even more care should be given to each husbandry technique.

Stock is normally planted at 12.5cm each way, throughout the year, and produc-tion factors (ie the number of cuttings/plant/week) have been worked out on this basis over a number of years. However after the rooted cuttings are planted and watered-in, stock management differs considerably from cut flower management.

Labelling

It is essential to identify every variety clearly with a label large enough to be eas-ily read when stock has reached a height of 50cm.

When planting care should be taken to keep varieties within families apart and always to allow a space between different varieties.

When taking cuttings it is necessary to write a label for each box of cuttings.

A lot of time can be saved by placing labels pre-written with the variety name in a container like a plastic cup fixed to the main variety label.

WATERING & LIGHTING

Sprayline watering will normally be used in the early stages but as soon as cutting taking begins it is best to have a low level irrigation system for two reasons. First, from the hygiene point of view, conditions will be less conducive to the spread of fungal diseases if foliage is kept as dry as possible. Second, it is a mistake to take wet cuttings as these will not store as long as dry ones. Sprayline watering combined with dull, cool weather can leave foliage too wet for cutting taking for hours and much production time will be lost.

Rates of application

Generally stock will require higher rates of water application than cut flowers particularly after the first few weeks of growth, up to double the quantity for mature stock plants in summer conditions. If cuttings become hard to snap it is almost certain to be due to a lack of water leading to fibrous cell production in the cortex of the stem too near the tips of the shoots. It is wise to test frequently for water with a soil auger to make sure that premature hardening does not occur.

Night-break lighting

Details of night-break lighting are given in chapter 2 (page 10). Lighting for stock plants is especially important as failure to keep the stock vegetative will lead to widescale premature budding.

Because it is vital to keep stock vegetative at all times, and taking into account that there will be different heights of plant in the stock house, the safest rates of night-break lighting should be used.

Lighting installations should provide not less than 100 lux illuminance and if cyclic lighting is used 50% half-hour cycles is the minimum requirement.

Supplementary light

Cuttings production will fall below one cutting per plant per week unless supplementary light is used from mid-October to mid-March in southern England. High pressure sodium lamps (SON/T) spaced to provide 2,000 lux at crop height are adequate. They must be sited so that they do not shade plants from the night-break lighting.

Generally lamps will be on from 4am to 4pm (0400-1600) daily, but on sunny days a saving can be made by switching off for a few hours.

Supplementary lighting will also improve the quality of cuttings which will subsequently benefit the crop's take-off and early growth.

NUTRITION

The objectives with chrysanthemum stock plant production are to keep plants growing strongly but preventing growth becoming either too soft or too hard. Hard growth will make cuttings difficult to snap, reduce production and cause uneven rooting. Soft growth will encourage botrytis and will sometimes prevent the cuttings from budding fast enough in poor light.

This fairly narrow optimum path can be trodden with correct nutrition bearing in mind that a chrysanthemum stock plant should always be in a strongly growing vegetative condition and does not have to be conditioned for flower bud initiation. The mistake some propagators make is to use high levels of potassium relative to nitrogen. High potassium to, say, $1N : 3K_2O$ in the soil will lead to hard, slow and gray-green growth. The resultant cuttings will be more difficult to root and respond more slowly to short-day conditions. The ideal N to K_2O ratio for stock plant production is $2N : 1K_2O$ and certainly no less than $3N : 2K_2O$; this applies on a year-round basis.

Cuttings produced from plants fed with a $3N : 1K_2O$ ratio will root much faster than others. Nitrogen is the element most rapidly leached from cuttings when rooted under mist and it is essential to ensure adequate supplies to the stock plants.

Soft growth misconception

Soft growth is often quite wrongly associated with high nitrogen levels when in fact it is often excessive water and lack of nutrient or disproportionate nutrition which produces the condition.

Stock plants fed with 300 ppm N and 100 ppm K_2O will produce cuttings with small dark green leaves which snap readily. On the other hand stock fed with 100 ppm N and 300 ppm K_2O will tend to have large grey-green leaves and wiry stems.

In an experiment some years ago, the author grew batches of stock in five different nutrition regimes:

1   High balanced 250 ppm N : 150 ppm K_2O
2   Medium balanced 175 ppm N : 100 ppm K_2O
3   Starvation
4   High nitrogen 250 ppm N : 50 ppm K_2O
5   High potassium 100 ppm N : 300 ppm K_2O

Suitable feeds of N and K_2O were applied to each stock nutrition regime to maintain each treatment. All other nutrients – phosphate, magnesium, calcium, etc – were applied normally. It was clear that treatment 4 was best for stock followed by treatment 1. In the author's experience, most stock plant nutrition regimes in practice resemble treatment 5 as far as nitrogen and potassium are concerned.

Although nitrogen feeding must be given priority, other elements of nutrition are important. When potassium levels are particularly high it is difficult for magnesium to be taken up by stock plants and deficiency symptoms can be seen even in cuttings in the rooting bench or very soon afterwards.

Similarly iron levels are often too low and iron deficiency is almost immediately present in the rooting cuttings particularly when leaching is excessive. In any varieties which may be prone to this problem, watering with magnesium sulphate and iron chelate during rooting quickly replaces the deficient elements and greens up the young plants. However it is best to feed stock correctly in the first place and ensure a good start to the crop.

Soil analysis prior to planting stock is absolutely essential and a suitable base dressing will balance the nutrients correctly. Thereafter a monthly plant sap analysis, using the oldest but still green leaves, will indicate the liquid feeding required to maintain balanced nutrient levels in the shoots.

It is a good maxim that the flowering crop begins when the stock plants are planted. This is particularly true in regard to nutrition. As an example of this, the author has been able to link, with statistical significance, the length of the pedicel of the cut flower variety Polaris, with the nitrogen nutrition of the stock plant. Because the time from taking cuttings to flowering pot plants is less compared with cut flowers, correct nutrition for pot plant stock is especially important. Also the faster the programme (or the shorter the time between taking the cutting and the harvesting of the flowers) the more important stock plant management, especially nutrition, will become.

TREATMENTS

Spraying for pests and diseases is especially important with stock plant management for obvious reasons.

The aim of fungicide application is to cover the leaves and stems with protective chemicals to prevent the outbreak of disease. Shoots on stock plants grow extremely fast so very frequent fungicide application is necessary; in good conditions, for example, the interval between flushes of cuttings is only 18 days.

The standard recommendation for flower crops is to spray every 10-14 days. For stock plants fungicide applications every seven days is more likely to prevent infection. This interval must, of course, be considered relative to the phytotoxicity of the chemical, as spraying with some chemicals every seven days will prematurely harden growth.

B-Nine (daminozide) application

Some chrysanthemum varieties produce excessive internodes, in particular the first after pinching which must be reduced by B-Nine application. This is to prevent stock becoming too tall too quickly and to give control over the length of the rooting cuttings. Generally applications of 0.0625% weekly during poor light periods will be sufficient.

Remember, however, that during a typical week stock plants will have been watered twice and may have been sprayed once with B-Nine and certainly once with a fungicide/pesticide application. Following the B-Nine spray the plants must remain dry for 24 hours to facilitate the uptake of the chemical. In order to maximise the time in which staff can take cuttings, the watering and spraying have to be carefully timed. If possible one of the weekend days, or both if necessary, can be used, one for spraying, one for watering.

Supporting

Stock can be left in production for up to 15 weeks in summer and 20 weeks in winter. If time to take cuttings is added, the life of a stock plant varies from 20 to 27 weeks. It is essential, therefore, for adequate plant support to be available and the same type of net used for supporting cut flower crops is satisfactory.

Pinching

Pinching describes the act whereby the growing tip is removed from the plant to encourage growth from lateral shoots. Stock plants are pinched to provide the maximum number of uniform shoots for cuttings. The timing of the pinch will affect the uniformity of the first flush of cuttings.

Each stock plant must be pinched between 10 and 14 days after planting to provide the first flush of cuttings. The plant must be well established and growing away before pinching and it is best to pinch all plants at the same time to avoid problems with taking cuttings later.

The aim is to produce a uniform batch of cuttings but the plant will have a natural apical dominance. Plants pinched too hard will tend to exhibit more apical dominance and the first shoot will grow much more rapidly than the second or third shoot. Equally it is a waste of time to allow too much growth before pinching and if plants are pinched too high the basal shoots will eventually grow through the stock and give cuttings which bud prematurely.

The correct method is to pinch to about eight leaves in winter and six or seven in summer. Plants should never be pinched into hard wood. If growth is hard, pinching should be left for a further few days.

It is important to make sure that the tip is removed completely as some workers tend to nip the leaves but fail to remove the growing point.

TAKING CUTTINGS

Taking cuttings is the most important operation in the year-round chrysanthemum growing production system. Since the early 1960's many growers have relied on commercial propagators for quality rooted and unrooted cuttings, supplied weekly in large quantities. Usually the quality of cuttings has been good although not always consistent. Lack of uniformity in size between cuttings to be grown side by side in dense populations is one of the main factors affecting quality and waste in the flowering product, especially pot chrysanthemums.

The problem for the self-propagator is twofold. First, it is essential to understand exactly the nature of the physical requirements of an unrooted cutting. Second, and more difficult to do, is to teach the cutting takers the best way to achieve the optimum requirement consistently, hour after hour, day after day, yet maintain a high rate of production – about 1,500/hour on commercial propagation nurseries.

The ideal cutting

• The wet weight of the cutting should be between 1.5 and 2.0g
• It should contain two semi-mature and two small leaves, the smallest of which will be about 30mm in length
• There should be a healthy vegetative growing point.
• The base of the cutting should be approximately 4 or 5mm in diameter with a 'leg' of about 12 to 15mm between the base and the lowest leaf
• The cutting should be sufficiently soft in growth to have been snapped cleanly with no torn or crushed tissue and with no fibre cells in the stem cortex to interfere with root growth from the cambium layer

The unrooted cutting

Apart from being free from pests and diseases, having an adequate and balanced nutrient content and representing the best clone of the correct variety, there are optimum physical characteristics for cuttings of each variety. It is, however, possible to give a general definition of a good cutting, taking into account any variety differences – see panel.

The most important factors in ensuring uniform growth in a batch of cuttings during and after rooting, are that the cuttings should have a similar weight and leaf area. Cuttings which have the same wet weight will tend to be similar in dry weight (ie contain an equivalent amount of nutrient for further growth). Cuttings which have a similar leaf area will, if treated equally during rooting and in the long-day phase, assimilate similar amounts of plant food by photosynthesis and will grow uniformly.

Critical judgement

In order to achieve this objective commercial propagators teach their staff to use 'taking discs' to ensure that cuttings of similar length are removed from the stock plants. But this assumes that cuttings of a similar length are of a similar weight and leaf area and explains the lack of uniformity of growth in many batches of cuttings! Cuttings which are taken to a definite length dictated by a taking disc and graded in no other way before despatch ought to be re-graded either visually or by weight.

Over many years the author has taken cuttings in several different ways and after growing on and measuring for uniformity at the start of short-day treatment has come to a very definite conclusion regarding the training of cutting takers. Because it is the weight and the leaf area of the cutting rather than length that is important, cuttings must be taken with the taker viewing the stock plants from almost directly above. It is only in this position that the size of the shoot (weight) and the leaf area can be accurately judged.

Viewed from above different sizes of shoot will be readily visible and those of the correct size mentally recorded. Reliance on a taking disc means the cutting taker must view the stock more from the side than from above in order to place the disc in the correct position. But it is very difficult to judge the weight of the cutting and its leaf area from the side.

Judging leaf area and weight and taking by eye will almost certainly result in cuttings of pot varieties of about 4 to 4.5cm in length with four leaves. There will only be 0.5cm variation in length in the batch of cuttings and this is not important provided the weight and leaf area is uniform.

How many in the hand?

When taking cuttings from above the crop it is a simple matter to select the uniform shoots, to place the top of the index finger against the fourth (lowest) leaf of the cutting and with the thumb to snap the cutting inwards so that it finishes inside the cupped hand. In this way up to 10 cuttings can be taken in one hand before having to be transferred to the other.

Most men and some women can hold 50 cuttings in the left hand while taking with the right (or vice versa). Placing the index finger at the position of the basal leaf ensures that a 'leg' equal to the width of the finger will be left on the cutting. This is ideal for sticking into the rooting medium so that the base leaf remains above the top of the medium.

This method of taking cuttings is also superior to the disc method from the production aspect as it requires more time to place the disc in the correct position before snapping than it does to place the finger alone in position. There could be a difference in taking rate of several hundred cuttings an hour.

One of the most important points relating to the taking of cuttings is the amount of time that elapses between placing them in the polythene bag (lettuce bags are excellent for the purpose) and getting them into the cold store. Cuttings in a plastic bag exposed in a glasshouse to full sunlight will be physically damaged by excessive heat within minutes.

It is good practice to place the bags in the shade of stock plants with the tops open until about 500 cuttings have been taken. The bags can then be sealed and boxed and taken immediately to the cold store or placed in a small mobile cooler inside the glasshouse.

Rooting hormones

Rooting hormones promote the rooting of cuttings of slightly difficult or 'hard' varieties by about three days. In ideal rooting conditions the whole cycle of sterilising rooting benches and/or floors, sticking, rooting and transferring to the production area can, with the use of rooting hormone, be completed two weeks round the year.

The obvious point in the cycle to apply rooting hormone powder is when 50 cuttings are conveniently held in a bundle prior to placing them in their plastic bag Only the base of the cutting needs to be powdered and much expensive hormone can be wasted if the container used is overfilled and the basal leaves of the cutting are also dipped.

Most proprietary hormones for softwood cuttings containing indolylbutyric acid (IBA) are excellent for the purpose at a strength 0.1% W/W of active ingredient.

Liquid hormones have been developed and are perfectly satisfactory for rooting. They have the disadvantage of the problem of disease spread if 50 cuttings are continually dipped into the same jar of liquid.

Long-day budding

All varieties of chrysanthemum will eventually produce a flower bud in long-day conditions even if this bud cannot develop to flowering. This unwanted bud, if present in an otherwise vegetative cutting, will cause low crowning and spoil the quality of the cut flower.

Varieties differ in their potential for long-day budding which is measured by either the number of leaves produced on a shoot prior to budding or by the growing time taken to reach budding potential.

It is clear, therefore, that all cuttings must be removed when they are ready. Delay in taking may lead to unwanted buds especially in pot varieties which tend to have low long-day leaf numbers.

The long-day leaf numbers of pot varieties tend to be in the low twenties. However, because all pot cuttings are pinched to eight to 10 leaves this is not normally a problem. If, however, cuttings are taken from long sheets some plants may 'break' earlier than the pinch and uneveness will result. In winter there is less problem because long-day leaf numbers increase on each variety as light becomes more limiting.

Cuttings procedure

The first flush of cuttings on the stock are the most difficult to take. If pinched correctly the stock plant will produce up to four cuttings within a period of a week from the first flush in summer. Generally at the first take only one or two of these cuttings will be sufficiently mature to remove leaving two leaves back on the shoot for further cuttings production.

The third cutting will reach maturity within a few days, followed immediately by the fourth. A fifth cutting from the first flush may be taken just prior to the start of the second flush.

The second flush

The second flush will be ready approximately 18 days after the start of the first flush in summer conditions. It is usually only the top two or three cuttings of the first flush which have a bare length of stem between the point of the pinch and the first leaf of the cutting. Thereafter it can be assumed that one or two leaves will have formed near to the base of the shoot and cuttings can be taken more quickly without checking to ensure that two leaves remain on each shoot after taking.

Frequency of taking

To obtain maximum output and uniformity of cuttings from a bed of stock, cuttings should be taken every two days in periods of maximum growth. In practice, however, it is often not possible to achieve more than two takes a week because of the management problem of having to apply B-Nine and a fungicide/aphicide spray on separate occasions, water twice and still leave the shoots dry for taking cuttings. The latter point is important as wet cuttings do not store well.

Taking cuttings twice rather than once a week will not only improve productivity substantially but it has a much more important function. Three to four days after taking cuttings there will be a substantial number of cuttings of the correct quality which, if removed at once, will leave only two to four leaves on the shoots from which they were taken. This not only reduces the risk of long-day leaf buds (see panel, page 70), but ensures that stock plants do not become too tall too fast.

Each take will normally only add about 5cm to the height of the stock.

If cuttings are not taken at the ideal time and long shoots remain after taking, not only is there a greater risk of long-day leaf buds but the shoots will have to be snapped back – an extra job – to keep the stock in good condition and prevent premature lengthening.

Removing cuttings twice weekly means that grading is done on a time basis. Thin cuttings remaining after the first take will fatten up and be ready for the second take of the week and so on. This is quite normal in summer production. In winter some shoots will always be thinner than others and it may be necessary to go over the stock twice each time of taking to separate the grades.

PLANNING STOCK

There is nothing difficult about planning stock but there are some basic facts regarding stock plant performance which need to be known before it can begin:

• time from planting stock to the production of cuttings

• period of production of cuttings from a stock plant at a given planting time

• production factors in terms of cuttings per plant per week at a given spacing

These three main factors will, of course, vary slightly according to the location of the stock area and the figures given below relate to a stock area based in Sussex or Hampshire. Production factors vary widely with variety and precise details for each variety are outside the scope of this book.

Time from planting to production   Assuming that rooted vegetative cuttings are planted at 12.5 x 12.5cm (61.6 plants/sq m) there are four such time periods in southern England:

Stock planted	Weeks to unrooted cuttings
1 November to mid-January	7
2 Mid-January to mid-February and October	6
3 Mid-February to end March, mid-August to end September	5
4 April to mid-August	4

During periods 1 and 2 stock plants are pinched two weeks after planting, in period 3 ten days after planting, and in period 4 seven days after planting.

Period of production These periods are fairly arbitrary but are based on the stock plants' ability to produce uniform and high quality cuttings which snap easily. Stock plants age more rapidly in high light conditions because of a rapid growth rate so that the period of useful life of a stock plant is longer in winter than in summer.

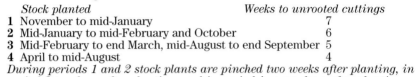

Examples of stock plant production periods

Batch	Plant week	Production period	(Weeks)
1	39	44 to 11	(20)
2	12	17 to 28	(12)
3	29	34 to 49	(16)

Yield of cuttings
from stock at 61.6 plants/sq m

	Cuttings per plant per week
January	0.9
February	1.0
March	1.2
April	1.3
May	1.4
June	1.5
July	1.5
August	1.4
September	1.4
October	1.2
November	1.0
December	0.9

Continuous planting of stock in this example gives three crops of stock in 63 weeks with an actual production period of 48 weeks (76%). Of course production periods can be curtailed to cope with short requirement period varieties, or increased slightly as convenient if stock management is of a sufficient standard.

Production factors   These vary greatly between categories of varieties, eg Princess Anne which was a cut flower converted to pot production and specially bred pot varieties. Detailed records are necessary before exact production figures can be given for each variety in each area but table left will help overall planning consideration. Most purpose-bred pot chrysanthemums, because of the nature of their well-branched habit, are good cuttings producers and some will improve the figures given in the table by up to 30%.

The figures above will only be correct if all cuttings are removed from the stock plants as soon as they are mature.

Stock planning

Weeks of production

	1	2	3	4	5	6	7	8	9	10	11	12	13	14	15	16	17	18	19	20	21	22	23	24	25	26	27	28	29	30	31
A	0.9	0.9	0.9	0.9	0.9	1.0	1.0	1.0	1.0	1.2	1.2	1.2	1.2	1.3	1.3	1.3	1.3	1.4	1.4	1.4	1.4	1.4	1.5	1.5	1.5	1.5	1.5	1.5	1.5	1.5	1.5
B	5.0	5.0	5.0	5.0	5.0	5.0	5.0	7.0	6.0	7.0	6.0	7.0	6.0	7.0	6.0	7.0	6.0	7.0	6.0	7.0	6.0	7.0	6.0	7.0	6.0	7.0	6.0	5.0	6.0	5.0	6.0
C														5.0												5.5					
D	5.5	5.5	5.5	5.5	5.5	6.0	6.0	6.0	6.0	7.0	7.0	7.0	7.0	8.0	8.0	8.0	8.0														
E																		6.5	6.5	6.5	6.5	7.0	7.0	7.0	7.0	7.0	7.0	7.0	7.0		7.5
F																															

All figures are thousands of plants
Total programme plus stock requirement (weeks 1–31) = 191,000
Total unrooted cuttings production (weeks 1–31) = 201,500 (wastage about 5%)
Stock planted week 46 allowed 18 weeks of production. Stock planted week 15 allowed 12 weeks of production

Key:
A = Stock production factor   **B** = Programme requirement   **C** = Stock requirement
D = Production figures from 6,000 stocks planted in week 46
E = Production figures from 4,650 stocks planted in week 15
F = Production figure from 5,000 stocks planted in week 26

Factors below 1 cutting/plant/week are not really acceptable since stock area in the winter needs to be increased. To prevent this, and to improve cutting quality, it is now normal to use supplementary light to provide an extra 2,000 lux for 12 hours a day between October and March.

Actual planning is achieved by using a large sheet of paper and filling in the requirements for unrooted cuttings for a year for each variety starting at least six months ahead.

The table above shows part of the annual planning outline for a typical pot plant variety such as Miramar.

Accurate recording is essential, especially when growing a new variety for the first time. It is a simple matter to give each cutting taker a notebook in which is entered date, variety, bed number and number of cutting. At the end of each week the data can be entered in a master stock list:

Variety	Bed No.	No. stock	Date planted	Cuttings production weeks			
				1	2	3	4

When stock is discarded the total number of cuttings taken divided by the weeks of production, divided by the number of stock plants will give the cuttings production factor for the whole period.

Use of a cold store

Healthy dry cuttings will store at 1-4C for three weeks and sometimes for a longer period provided cuttings are insulated from drying out.

The cuttings should be removed from the stock area and placed in the cold store as soon as possible after taking, particularly in hot weather. The heat generated in a plastic bag filled with 50 unrooted cuttings on a hot summer day is considerable. This field heat must be removed rapidly by cold storage, otherwise damage will occur and cuttings will rot during storage. Containers which allow good cold air circulation to all bags of cuttings are ideal.

Cuttings raised in England benefit from a period of cold storage prior to sticking because the base of the cutting requires a period of time to lignify before sticking. A period of one week is generally sufficient so that it is usual to plan cuttings production for at least one week before the cuttings are required.

The cold store can also be used to smooth out slight undulations in requirements during periods when cuttings production is stable, ie neither increasing in spring conditions or reducing in autumn conditions.

The size of the cold store should, of course, relate to the size of the programme and its requirements. An acre (0.4ha) of cut flowers requires about 12,000 cuttings a week.

Allowing for three weeks' supply of cuttings in store and by measuring the size of containers which hold 1,000 cuttings it is a simple matter to calculate the maximum size of store required, remembering to allow space for movement of personnel and sorting.

5 Pests & diseases

Fungal diseases. Bacterial diseases. Pests.

The environmental conditions provided for optimum growth of year round chrysanthemums also, unfortunately, provides an ideal environment for the many pests and diseases which attack the crop. In particular since the 1980's the use of thermal screens has increased humidity at night while carbon dioxide enrichment often increases humidity by day. As a consequence some fungal diseases have become more prevalent and more difficult to control.

This chapter deals with the main P&D disorders of chrysanthemums, describing them briefly and suggesting chemical controls. In the United Kingdom conventional chemical control measures for pests have become more important since the introduction of the western flower thrips for which, at the time of writing, there is no biological control system.

Chemical use

All rates of chemicals mentioned in the text refer to the amount of active ingredient and are in accordance with approved uses prevailing in the UK at the time of writing. Conditions and regulations in other countries may differ and users should check before applying. In any case, all crop protection materials should only be applied advisedly and in accordance with good practice and the law.

FUNGAL DISEASES

Most of the important diseases of chrysanthemums are fungal diseases. There are also a few important bacterial diseases – see page 79.

Botrytis

This pathogen affects all stages of growth but especially stems of cuttings in the rooting area and near the base of stems of more mature plants in the centre of solid benches where conditions are particularly humid. Infection occurs more easily through damaged tissue. On flowers botrytis is seen as brown, water soaked spots and is usually referred to as 'damping'.

Apart from decreasing the humidity, botrytis can be controlled by the following chemical sprays:

captan	100g/100 litres
thiophanate-methyl	50g/100 litres
dichlofluanid	50g/100 litres
thiram	300g/100 litres
benomyl	240g/100 litres
iprodion	100g/100 litres

Watering cuttings after sticking with captan 200g/100 litres or vinclozolin 100g/100 litres reduces rotting caused by botrytis.

Petal blight

This disease, caused by *Itersonilia perplexans*, is much less common than botrytis but is often masked by it. It occurs mainly on flowers of unheated crops; the tips of the petals turn brown and the rot spreads inwards irregularly. As with botrytis humidity control is important but sprays of zineb (125g/100 litres) should control the disease.

The use of some of the above chemicals as fine fogs on flowers affected with Botrytis and petal blight can be very effective provided its application is carefully carried out.

Powdery mildew

This is a common disease of chrysanthemums affecting the leaves caused by the fungus *Oidium chrysanthemi*. White powdery patches appear on upper leaf surfaces and the disease is particularly prevalent in draughty or dry corners of the greenhouse.

Control can be achieved by chemical sprays of:

triforine	30g/100 litres
thiophanate-methyl	50g/100 litres
pyrazophos	15g/100 litres
or as a carbendazin fungicide	25 to 30g/100 litres

Ray blight

This was regarded as a very serious disease when it first occurred on year round chrysanthemums in the 1960's. It is still a serious disease but with an understanding of its life-cycle and the regular use of chemical sprays, it has in general been successfully kept under control.

Ray blight (*Didymella chrysanthemi*) causes blackish lesions on stems and foliage of young plants and in flowering plants can spread from the point of infection in the ray florets to attack pedicels, leaves and stems which turn black. The main period of spread is during rooting when spores are washed from the leaves into the compost and enter the base of the cutting.

As ray blight is more resistant to heat than other diseases, rooting bench sterilisation should be controlled at a temperature of at least 90C for 20 minutes.

Cuttings should be watered in with mancozeb (80g/100 litres) and sprays of benomyl (50g/100litres), captan (100g/100 litres) and triforine (30g/100 litres) together with mancozeb have given control on older plants. The use of clean plant material is essential in the prevention of this disease.

Particularly vulnerable varieties such as Olnura and Criterion were discarded as a preventative measure many years ago.

Rhizoctonia

This disease attacks the base of young plants in warm moist conditions. Growth is retarded and the whole stem then collapses. Stem lesions are brown and dry.

Control is achieved by either drenching with thiram (150g/100 litres) or spraying with benomyl (240g/100litres).

Septoria

This is a leaf disease which is now relatively uncommon. It causes circular greyish-brown leaf spots but the symptoms are often masked by those of botrytis. Spraying with benomyl (25g to 50g/100 litres) will control septoria leaf spot.

Verticillium wilt

Verticillium albo-atrum is only a problem if bought in with the cuttings. Initial symptoms are stunted plants with interveinal chlorosis followed by a general wilting with leaves turning brown. Frequently, in good growing conditions, plants grow reasonably well until flower colour shows and then general wilting and necrosis follows rapidly.

In pots where even one infected plant is located these should be discarded at the earliest opportunity to prevent spread of the disease into matting, etc.

White rust

Japanese or chrysanthemum white rust, although not a notifiable disease, is still a serious threat to chrysanthemum producers. It is endemic in Europe and thus the continual shipments of flowers from Holland and cuttings from continental Europe and the Canary Islands pose a constant threat to chrysanthemum growers in countries like the UK. However because white rust can only survive on chrysanthemums, rigorous control measures can totally eradicate it from a nursery.

Symptoms are easily recognisable, even by growers who have never previously seen the disease.

Pale green to yellow sunken areas up to 4mm across appear on the upper surfaces of leaves and these areas eventually become dark brown to black. Directly below these indentations, underneath the leaves, prominent, raised pinkish-buff pustules develop which later become white. The pustules are tightly packed with teleutospores which generally germinate within the pustule to produce one to three sporidia. These are released and propelled into the air currents which spread the disease.

In favourable conditions the sporidia germinate and infect another leaf to give rise to a further generation of teleutospores. One of the main problems with white rust control is the unpredictability of its rate of spread which is governed very closely by environmental conditions. The incubation period between infection by sporidia and appearance of pustules on leaves can vary from two days in optimum conditions to over eight weeks (up to 14 weeks has been reported).

The discharge of sporidia occurs at a relative humidity of 96% and a film of water on the surface is essential for spore germination.

Spores will only survive for an hour at 90% RH or above and only for five minutes at 80% RH. From the practical point of view it follows that leaves should be kept as dry as possible and relative humidities below 90%. Watering should be done in the mornings as should spraying with insecticides, fungicides or B-Nine.

Optimum temperature for white rust is about 17C and leaf infection will not occur above 24C. Temperature is more important after infection has occurred – see table.

Since sporidia can survive up to an hour in humidities above 90% it is possible for the disease to spread from nursery to nursery in humid conditions where these are close together. The disease can also spread, in theory, on clothing or tools.

White rust regimes

Temperature	Incubation period
10C	13 days
17C	5 to 6 days
24C	up to 8 weeks

But probably 99% of outbreaks can be traced to infected plant material, cuttings or plants being introduced to the nursery.

It should be remembered that infected leaves will remain a source of sporidia if left lying on the benches.

Growers in high risk areas should take preventative measures against white rust especially during the main period of rust, April to October. Curative treatments which are reasonably effective are also often phytotoxic.

Work by Dickens at the Plant Pathology Laboratory, Harpenden, indicated that benodanil (150g/100 litres) (no longer available in the UK) gives better protection than either triforine (75ml/100 litres) or oxycarboxin (75g/100 litres). However the same researcher also showed that weekly oxycarboxin fogs interspersed with triforine sprays (150ml/100 litres) give very good protection and control without much phytotoxicity. Wet sprays of oxycarboxin, even with a non-ionic spreader, are phytotoxic when the spray falls on the soil or compost. However for some years now the most effective control has been the use of propicanazole (40g/100 litres) used up to three times at five-day intervals.

A further problem is that varieties which are resistant to one strain of white rust are not necessarily resistant to other strains so the Dutch policy of breeding for resistance may not be effective.

BACTERIAL DISEASES

Bacterial wilt

This is caused by *Erwinia chrysanthemi*, the symptoms being wilting of mature plants together with vascular discoloration and blackening of stems and leaves. Not common in the UK it has, however, been occasionally imported on cuttings.

Crown gall

Caused by the organism *Agrobacterium tumefaciens*, large galls are induced to form on the stems at compost level and sometimes on shoots and leaves. Plants are not destroyed by the galls but the latter appear to have a weakening effect.

Very little is known about crown gall.

Pseudomonas

Psuedomonas fluorescens was isolated from diseased chrysanthemum cuttings in 1970 and has, periodically, caused problems since then. Pseudomonas species are normally saprophytic only but it seems that when cuttings grown in southern latitudes are rooted in poor winter light conditions in northern Europe the bacteria multiply quickly and block the vascular tissues of the stem. The base of the cutting becomes hollow and takes on a reddish coloration and the infected plants are severely weakened.

Chemical control of these bacterial diseases is not yet possible and growers must rely on good environmental control, hygiene and the immediate destruction of all infected material.

PESTS

Most chrysanthemum growers – in the UK at least – still rely on chemical control of pests especially since the introduction of western flower thrips, but this is becoming more difficult as pest resistance to chemicals seems to build up more quickly than new chemical controls are formulated. In addition phytotoxicity between some chemicals and some chrysanthemum varieties is always a problem.

However with care growers can still achieve reasonable levels of pest control by chemical means alone.

Aphids

Aphids are pests for three reasons. Not only do they feed on the crop and cause damage to growing points but they transmit virus diseases and secrete honeydew deposits which attract fungal growth.

The most troublesome aphids on chrysanthemums are *Myzus persicae* (the peach-potato aphid) and *Aphis gossypii* (the cotton or melon aphid). *Myzus persicae* has developed widespread resistance to organophosphorus insecticides but may be controlled by direct contact with nicotine smokes or pirimicarb (25g/100 litres) sprays.

Aphis gossypii is now very resistant to pirimicarb and other carbamates but can still be controlled with nicotine smokes and dichlorvos (100ml/100 litres) sprays. Because the above sprays kill only by direct contact, spraying must be carried out very efficiently to reach all the aphids, many of which colonise under the leaves.

Caterpillars

Many species of caterpillars attack chrysanthemums. The most common in the UK are the caterpillars of the angleshade and silver Y moths. Sprays of carbaryl (75g/100 litres), diazinon (40g/100 litres) or trichlorphon (200g/100 litres) are effective controls and atomisation of dichlorvos (3.5g/100cu m) has given good control of young larvae.

Leafminer

The chrysanthemum leafminer, *Phytomyza syngenesiae*, can still readily be controlled by chemicals despite some resistance. Effective sprays are azinphos-methyl, bromophos, cartap, dimethoate, dioxathion, pirimiphos-methyl and trichlophon all at 100g/100 litres.

Another leaf miner, *Liriomyza trifolii*, was introduced into Britain in 1977 and is a notifiable pest. It has a wide host range which includes tomato plants.

It is distinguishable from *P. syngenesiae* by the yellow pupa which falls into the compost and does not remain in the leaf. In the UK incidence of this pest must be reported to the Ministry of Agriculture immediately and the authorised control measure instructions must be followed.

In the same category, and even more difficult to control is *Liriomyza huidobrensis*. Recent chemical controls are pyrazophos with xylene (50ml/100 litres), abamectin (20ml/100 litres) and triazophos with xylene (75ml/100 litres).

Red spider mite

This pest, *Tetranychus urticae*, will breed round the year because the natural winter diapause is inhibited by night-break lighting. All the systemic and many contact-acting pesticides available are now useless because of built-up resistance.

Cyhexatin sprayed at a rate of 25g/100 litres is one of the few effective contact chemicals for red spider mite control remaining. It is particularly useful because it does not harm the predatory mite *Phytoseiulus persimilis* used in biological control systems. Where chemical control only is relied on, abamectine (20ml/100 litres) and dicofol (200ml/100 litres) have given good results in recent years.

Thrips

Thrips tabaci can breed and feed on the growing points of chrysanthemums round the year but they remain easy to control by chemical means.

By far the most important pest of year-round chrysanthemums is the western flower thrips (*Frankliniella occidentalis*).

Because of its habit of pupating in the soil or compost and entering the flower soon after sepal split, it is extremely difficult to control. The incidence of western flower thrips has also led to an explosion of the virus disease tomato spotted wilt in chrysanthemums, which is rapidly spread by the thrips if they are not rigorously controlled.

High volume wet spray of dichlorvos (100 ml/100 litres) and/or malathion 60 (190ml/100 litres) will control these thrips but only if the chemical reaches them. This is extremely difficult to do when the pest is secure in the depths of a tightly incurving mass of petals.

The most effective control of western flower thrips has been to combine the use of sterilised compost and ultra low volume sprayers using dichlorvos. The latter treatment is usually applied every week round the year for best results.

BIOLOGICAL CONTROL

It is the incidence of western flower thrips that has severly restricted the use of biological control on chrysanthemums in recent years. It is an accepted fact that a percentage of pest will always remain on the plants (perhaps up to 10%).

However such is the damage inflicted by only a small population of thrips either by direct damage to flowers or indirectly by the symptoms of tomato spotted wilt, that total control of thrips has to be achieved. The chemicals used for this purpose, such as dichlorvos, not only control thrips but have a devastating effect on most of the parasites and predators used in biological control.

At the time of writing there are no large chrysanthemum growers in the UK using biological control and this is likely to remain the case in the foreseeable future. This is a pity, because there are now reliable biologicial controls available for use against all the main pests (see panel).

Biological controls

Parasites and predators available to chrysanthemum producers

Problem	Control
Aphids	Aphidus colemani
	Apidoletes aphidimyza
	Apidoletes hippodamia
Chrysodeixis chalcites	Bacillus thuringiensis
Leafminers	Dacnusa sibirica
	Diglyphus isaea
Red spider mites	Phytoseiulus persimilis
Spodoptera (Florida moth)	Spod-X
Thrips	Amblyseius cucumeris
	Orius
Whiteflies	Encarsia formosa

It is reported that some Dutch growers use biological controls on chrysanthemums in winter and spring, when thrips are less active, and resort to chemical control only from June to December. However this can be a dangerous practice because it cannot be predicted exactly when populations of pests will build up even when very careful monitoring is carried out and it always takes a little time for predators and parasites to become effective. Margins of profit tend to be low even in the most modern production systems so that crop managers have no choice but to keep absolute control of all major damaging pests and diseases by the use of chemicals.

Index

Dr Barrie Machin

The author was bitten by the chrysanthemum bug when, at the age of 11, he visited a leading amateur grower in Nottingham and saw large, exhibition blooms for the first time. Leaving school at 16, he was trained by the former head gardener at Boots' Lenton Experiment Station.

After National Service he spent four years at Nottingham University gaining an Honours Degree in Horticulture, the subject of his dissertation being 'The effects of light and temperatures on chrysanthemums'. This involved a study of all the literature relating to year-round chrysanthemums in the USA and led to his appointment as head propagator at Frampton's Leythorne Nursery, Chichester, in July 1956. Within a month he planted the first year-round chrysanthemum crop in England.

Rapidly growing interest in the crop led to his development of stock planting and production, flower production, advisory and plant health departments between 1957 and 1968. Due to the absence of good varieties for winter production, he became a breeder by necessity in 1963, Snowdon being one of his early varieties, along with Polaris and Fandango.

From 1968 to 1973 he researched and introduced a direct short-day planting technique at Frampton's which led directly to the peat block system of production used throughout Europe since the 1970's. This involved a detailed study of the effects of light, temperature, nutrition and clonal selection on the growth of stock plants and on flowering plants in both long-day and short-day regimes. For this work he gained his PhD from the University of Nottingham.

From 1974 he spent 12 years breeding chrysanthemums first at Perifleur Ltd and then as Barrie Machin Ltd where he continued as adviser to Frampton's Cuttings Ltd.

Since 1986 he has been breeder and technical director of Goldstock Breeding, a division of Southern Glasshouse Produce Ltd, at Swallowfield Nurseries, Titchfield, Hampshire, UK. In this capacity he also travels the world as a chrysanthemum consultant.